LONGMAN KEY SKILLS

LEVEL

3

WITHDRAWN

WITHDRAWN

Series editor: Barry Smith

WITHDRAWN

Longman

Rotherham College of Arts and Technology

R52187

Longman Key Skills
titles available in the series

Application of Number Level 1+2
Application of Number Level 3

Communication Level 1+2
Communication Level 3

Information Technology Level 1+2
Information Technology Level 3

Pearson Education Limited
Edinburgh Gate, Harlow
Essex CM20 2JE, England
and Associated Companies throughout the world

© DB associates 2000

The right of DB associates to be identified as authors of this work has been asserted by them in accordance with the Copyright, Designs and Patents Act 1988

All rights reserved; no part of this publication may be reproduced, stored in any retrieval system, or transmitted in any form or by any means, electronic, mechanical, photocopying, recording, or otherwise without either the prior written permission of the Publishers or a licence permitting restricted copying in the United Kingdom issued by the Copyright Licensing Agency Ltd, 90 Tottenham Court Road, London W1P 0LP.

First published 2000
Second impression 2000

British Library Cataloguing in Publication Data
A catalogue entry for this title is available from the British Library

ISBN 0-582-42487-9

Set by 3 in Sabon and Quay Sans
Printed in Malaysia, KVP

Contents

RCAT
LIBRARY & LEARNING
RESOURCES CENTRE
Acc. No. RS2187
22/11/05 P
CLASS: 510

How to use this book

This book helps you obtain the key skill called Application of Number Level 3. You will be doing your key skills with your other studies in a school, college or at work. The common combinations are:

Level 3
A-level and key skills
Vocational A-level and key skills

An Application of Number key skill is not the same as maths. It is about knowing some facts about graphics, numbers or calculations and showing that you can actually use them in real life. Most of us need a reminder about some of those forgotten words and ideas so this book is organised to provide rapid help when you want it.

The good news about gaining any of the key skills is that you don't always need to do extra work. The evidence for the key skill is produced while you are doing your normal study and work such as in the classroom, laboratory, workshop, or while working at a job.

Of course there is a certain cunning in knowing which of your work to keep and how to show it, and that's what this is book is about. There are special sections for all popular A-level and Vocational A-level subjects which tell you exactly what you need to do.

You can use this book in different ways; it depends on what you need. For example you might not need to read it from the beginning. To get the most out of this book, have a look at the following summary of how it is organised and decide how you can use it best.

The GNVQ Advanced awards are now called **Vocational A-levels**.

From September 2001 GNVQ Foundation and Intermediate awards are likely to be known as **Vocational GCSEs**.

Part 1: The Learning Curve

This part of the book concentrates on what you need to know to get the key skill units. It has useful information about graphics, numbers and how to use them in practical situations. It concentrates on the more tricky ideas and has clear worked examples to show you how to use them.

You can check that you have the basic knowledge needed by the key skill units. If you are up to speed with your maths then you may not need much of this section.

Everyone will find the **Useful knowledge** boxes helpful – they contain short reminders of important words and ideas.

Part 2: The Bottom Line

This part of the book tells you what you must do to gain the key skills units. It explains:

- The words and ideas of the key skills
- The definition of level 3
- How you can practise the skills
- What must be in your portfolio of evidence

Your collection of evidence or portfolio is the key to getting your key skill. This part of the book tells you how to choose your evidence and get it ready.

Part 3: Opportunities

This part of the book tells you where to find opportunities for evidence in the study or work you are already doing. If you are at school or college you should look up the pages for your particular subjects at A-level or Vocational A-level.

Everyone should look at the chapter on **Evidence from everyday sources**. It has examples of everyday activities we do at home, at work or at play that can also be used as evidence.

Margin

Look in the margin for simple explanations of important words and ideas and for references to other places in the book where there is useful information.

Part 1: The Learning Curve

This part concentrates on what you need to know to get your key skills qualification. It will show you:

- How to use numbers and graphics in practical situations.
- Whether you are up to speed with the basic knowledge needed for number key skills.
- Clear explanations of the more difficult ideas.

This part is divided into five sections:

- **Graphics**
- **Numbers**
- **Data**
- **Measuring and observing**
- **Calculations**

You will also find the **Useful Knowledge** boxes helpful – they contain quick reminders of the most important words and ideas.

Graphics

This chapter shows you how to use tables, charts, diagrams, graphs or other graphical displays. You already use graphical displays in your daily life whenever you read a timetable or look at a map or plan. You need to know about different ways of presenting information clearly and simply and you also need to know how to read, understand and interpret graphical displays so that you can use them to present your own information.

For quick reminders see the **Useful Knowledge** boxes

Using tables

A table is a useful method of presenting information or data in a way that can be quickly and easily understood. A table consists or rows and columns, with headings and labels. The labels tell you what is stored in the table and help you identify what is being shown. The following table is from a holiday brochure showing the maximum temperature each month for different places in the world.

Temperature (°C)

	Jan	Feb	Mar	Apr	May	Jun	Jul	Aug	Sep	Oct	Nov	Dec
London	6	7	10	13	17	20	22	21	19	14	10	7
Miami	23	24	26	27	29	30	31	31	31	28	26	24
Sydney	26	26	25	22	19	17	16	18	20	22	24	25

Using charts

Types of chart
pictogram
bar chart
pie chart
frequency diagram
scatter diagram

A chart is a diagram which shows relationships between numbers in a variety of graphical ways, described below. Charts are useful for giving rapid visual information about data but, like graphs, their accuracy depends upon the size of their scales. A chart can also be misleading if it doesn't give you information such as where the starting point is.

Bar charts

Bar charts or bar graphs are a useful way of comparing information in a form that catches the eye. The following bar chart 1 uses the height of the bars to compare the maximum daily temperature in London and other cities for different months. If you need to, you can read the actual temperature from the scale on the vertical axis. The bars can be vertical or horizontal, they can be separated by spaces or placed next to each other.

Bar charts can have the bars vertical or horizontal.

Computer spreadsheets are designed to handle tables, graphs and charts. Enter your data in a table on the spreadsheet and the software allows you to display that data in a choice of charts and graphs.

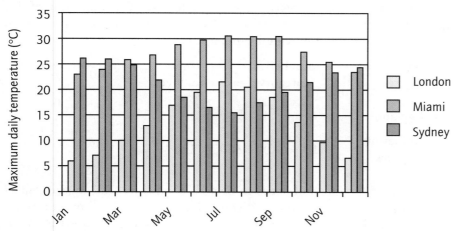

Pie charts

A pie chart, as the name suggests, shows how information or data has been shared out. The chart always uses a circle which is divided into sectors (like the portions of a pie) to show how different amounts compare, or sliced up like a pie to show who has the most or the least. The full circle is 100% and the amount of each item shown is proportional to the angle or 'slice of pie' used to show the item. Some versions of pie charts show some slices of the pie in different colours or partly drawn out (exploded). Here is a pie chart of travel destinations.

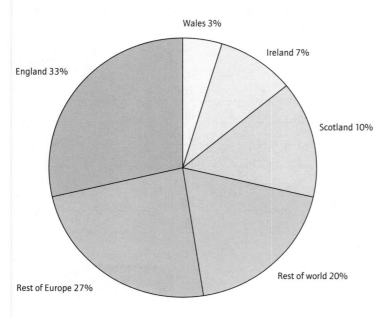

To make a pie chart you can use the graphics of a spreadsheet, or you can calculate the size of each sector of the pie. The first thing you need to know is that a circle is made up of 360°. The circle represents the total number of things you are working with; here it is a total of 30 people interviewed about travel destinations. The size of each slice depends upon the numbers for each category; for example, the 10 people (out of 30) going to England make one slice. To find out the size of this slice in degrees, you use the following formula:

$$\text{number of degrees} = \left(\text{number in category} \div \text{total number} \right) \times 360$$

For England:

$$\text{number of degrees} = (10 \div 30) \times 360 = 120$$

So the sector for England needs to be a slice which is 120° in size, out of a total of 360°. To measure 120° you will need to use a protractor and it should look like $\frac{1}{3}$ of a circle. It doesn't matter where you start a sector. You should also do a calculation like this for each category. You can check if your calculations are correct before drawing the pie chart by adding up all your answers. They should total 360°.

Frequency diagrams

A frequency diagram is a form of bar chart. When information is collected for statistics, the frequency is the number of times a particular measurement occurs. The following table shows the travel destinations of a group of people. The number of people for each destination is the frequency of that destination. This information is often shown in a **frequency diagram**. In this case you can quickly see the popularity of a destination from the lengths of the bars.

Tally marks are grouped in 5's

A **tally** is a stroke on a table to record the answer from one person. The fifth stroke is slanted to finish a group of a number. *See also*: **Data**, page 18.

Destination	Tally	Frequency
England	＋＋＋ ＋＋＋	10
Ireland	‖	2
Scotland	‖‖	3
Wales	‖	1
Rest of Europe	＋＋＋ ‖‖	8
Rest of World	＋＋＋ ‖	6
Total		30

Count the tallies to give the frequency

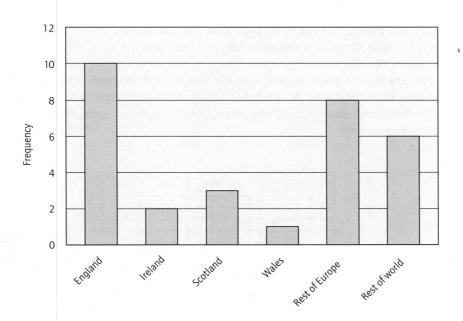

Using simple graphs

A graph is a type of diagram which shows how two different quantities, or **variables**, relate to each other. The numbers are laid out on axes at the

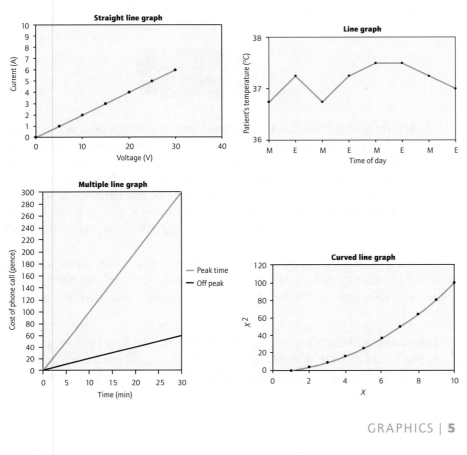

side of the graph and the relationship is usually shown by a continuous line. This line is often a straight line but can also be a curve for some relationships.

The graph is a good way of quickly finding information and also for changing from one unit to another. This temperature conversion graph shows how temperatures in degrees Celsius relate to temperatures in degrees Fahrenheit.

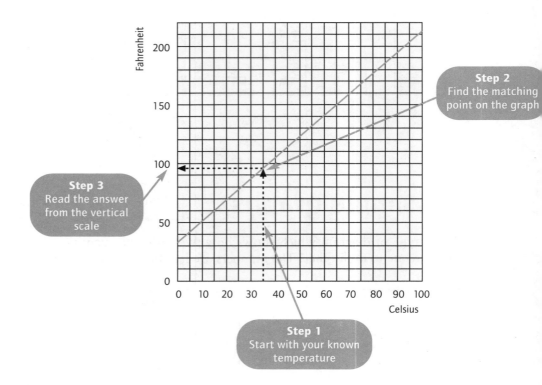

Step 2
Find the matching point on the graph

Step 3
Read the answer from the vertical scale

Step 1
Start with your known temperature

Axes: the two straight lines, at right angles, which have the scale of numbers.
x-axis: the horizontal scale.
y-axis: the vertical scale.
Scale: the numbers and spacing marked along the axes.

There are also formulas which convert between temperatures but using a line graph is usually quicker and easier. The example shows how you can convert 60 °C to 140 °F. You need to read up vertically from the 60 on the Celsius scale at the bottom and make a mark on the slanting line. From that mark you need to read across horizontally to the Fahrenheit scale on the side. Because the scale can't show every number, you will often have to read in between the scale and decide, using your eye, what the final answer is.

When you read a graph upwards or across you must make sure the reading is exactly vertical or exactly horizontal. Most graphs have a grid of lines to help you do this but if there aren't enough lines then use a ruler.

Take care! Although a graph is convenient to use, it is limited in accuracy by the size of its scale, and also depends upon how good *you* are at using it. Always repeat your use of the graph to see if your get the same answer.

Drawing graphs

A graph is produced after plotting pairs of coordinates as points on a grid. The following table shows the results of reading someone's body temperature twice each day. They can be plotted as pairs of points as a group. In fact, you have already seen this graph on page 5.

Time of day	M	E	M	E	M	E	M	E
Patient temp.	36.8	37.2	36.8	37.2	37.4	37.4	37.2	37.0

The graph is produced using the following rules:

- The item that can be controlled, the time of day, is read from the x-axis (horizontal).
- The other variable, the temperature, is read from the y-axis (vertical).
- Where the two readings cross, a point is marked by a small dot or cross.
- The plotted points are joined up.

In the graph of body temperature a series of straight lines is a good way to show the changes in temperature. For some other data you would expect to drawn a smooth curve or straight line.

Scatter diagram

A scatter diagram, also called a scatter graph or scattergram, is used to find out whether there is a connection between two variables, such as height and weight. Because the numbers for height and weight exist in pairs, they can be plotted on a graph using x-axes and y-axes. The following graph plots the weight and height of eight people.

See also: **Data**, page 18.

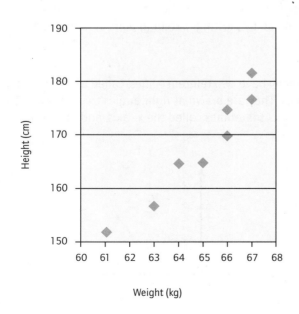

Correlation: the strength of connection between two sets of data; it can be strong, weak, or non-existent.

The investigation of the connection is made by looking at the scatter of the plotted points and judging if there is a trend between two sets of data. If there is a strong trend, or **correlation**, you will see an approximate straight line. If the correlation between the two sets of data is very strong, you can draw a **line of best fit**. Don't be afraid to use your eye – it is good at judging.

A scatter graph is equally useful in statistics for showing that there is *no* connection between sets of data. When the points are plotted and they show a random scatter, then there is no connection (no correlation).

USEFUL KNOWLEDGE

Pictogram
Pictograms use symbols to show how many units of data belong in a group.

Bar chart
Bar charts use the length of a bar against a scale to show how many units of data belong in a group.

Frequency diagram
A graphical way of showing the number of things counted in each group or type. Bar charts and pictograms are frequency diagrams.

Pie chart
A circular diagram where each group is shown as a slice or sector and the size of each sector shows the number of things counted in that group.

Line graph
A diagram which shows how information changes between consecutive values. The 'line' may be all straight, it may be straight between points on the graph, or it may curve.

Scatter diagram, scattergram, scatter graph
A diagram or graph which shows how two sets of numerical data are related. It is made by plotting matching pairs of numbers as points on a graph.

Axes
Graphs normally have two reference lines, called axes (one reference line is called an axis). They are drawn at right angles to each other. The horizontal axis is sometimes called the x–axis, and the vertical axis is often called the y-axis.

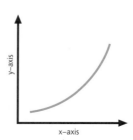

Variables

A variable is what you are measuring on your graph. You measure it because it can change – it is variable. For example, if you are showing the temperature each month, you measure the temperature because it changes and you plot it against the month the measurement was taken in. The non-changing variable is usually put on the *x*-axis. In this example the months don't change so they make a good *x*-axis.

Coordinates

Coordinates are pairs of numbers that plot a particular point on a graph. When a coordinate is quoted as (*a, b*) the rule is that *a* is the distance along the *x*-axis and the second number *b* is the distance along the *y*-axis.

Numbers

This chapter concentrates on some of the more difficult ideas of numbers that you are likely to come across in examples for your key skills. Included are negative numbers and how to express very large or very small numbers. A later section concentrates on calculating with numbers. The **Useful Knowledge** boxes have brief reminders of basic terms and ideas if you need them.

Negative numbers

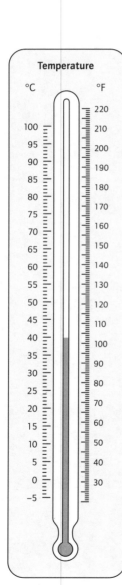

We sometimes need to describe things with negative numbers, also called directed numbers. We use a + (positive) sign or a − (negative) sign to label things which can go below zero, or below some other starting point. The temperature of the weather is an example where temperature can go below zero degrees Celsius. Another example of negative numbers is a bank account. The money in your account can be positive (the bank owes you) or negative (you owe the bank).

With negative numbers −5 is smaller than −2. This is not such a strange effect if you think in terms of owing money. Make sure you can calculate the difference in amount between these sorts of numbers.

What is the difference in temperature when the weather changes from −5 °C to +20 °C?

From −5 °C to zero the temperature rises by: 5 °C
From zero to +20 °C the temperature rise by: 20 °C
(usually we just write 20 °C and omit the +)
The total of the two temperature rises is: 25 °C
Check this on the thermometer diagram.

> **Take care!** You now use the sign − as shorthand for two different ideas:
> - When used in 4 − 3 = 1 it is an instruction to subtract.
> - When used in −20 °C indicates that the temperature is on the negative side of zero.

When you don't have a real scale like on a thermometer it is useful to make a **number line**. You use it to help you place numbers in order and to add or subtract them.

Shorthand signs
equals sign	=
decimal point	.
plus sign	+
minus sign	−
multiply sign	×
divide sign	÷ or /
percentage	%
ratio sign	:

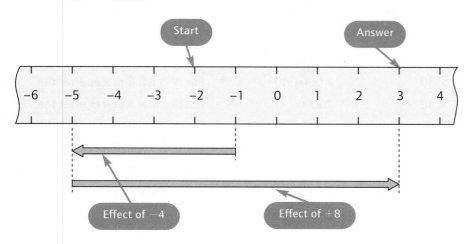

Find the result of combining −1, −4 and +8.
The number line shows how to work out the result:

* Start: at the −1 position
* For −4 move backwards (because negative) by 4 steps to the −5 position.
* For +8 move forwards (because positive) by 8 steps to the +3 position.
* So the answer is

$$(-1) + (-4) + (+8) = +3$$

Large and small numbers

If you multiply the two large numbers 2 000 000 and 3 000 000, you get the very large number 6 000 000 000 000. It is inconvenient to write down all those zeros and it is easy to make mistakes. The agreed way to write such a big number is 6×10^{12} (called 6 times 10 to the 12).

This method of writing large or small numbers in powers of 10 is called **standard form** or **scientific notation**. Using this method also avoids the confusion about exactly how much is meant by billion or trillion. Here are some rules for writing standard form:

* The first number is always between 1 and 10.
* The number on the 10 is called the **power** or the **index** or the **exponent**. It tells you how many places to move the decimal point.

1×10^6 means 1 000 000.

7×10^3 means 7000

4.2335×10^7 means 4.235 0000

Positive numbers are usually written **without** a plus sign, so 3 means that 3 is on the positive side of the number line.

See also: **Advanced calculators**, page 28.

The Learning Curve

See also: **SI unit prefixes**, page 24.

Power also means index form.
Exponent also means index form.

See also: **Advanced calculators**, page 28.

The system can also be used for writing very small numbers by using negative powers of 10. Note that 7000 (7×10^3) can also be written as 7k where k stands for kilo. You will see this in advertisements for computer memory, and in advertisements for jobs with large salaries! Here are some more examples.

Standard form	Number	Notes
1×10^6	1 000 000	Put decimal 6 places after the 1
7×10^3	7000	Put decimal 3 places after the 7
4.235×10^7	42 350 000	Put decimal 7 places after the 4
2×10^{-2}	0.02	Put decimal 2 places before the 2
1.673×10^{-27} kg	a very small number	Mass of one hydrogen atom
5.980×10^{25} kg	a very large number	Mass of planet earth

Fractions decimals and percentages

Fractions decimals and percentages are different ways of showing that we only have part of a whole. You already know some of these relationships and it is worth remembering the following common ones. The decimals one-third and two-thirds are given to 3 decimal places.

	Fraction	Decimal	Percentage
One-tenth	$\frac{1}{10}$	0.1	10%
One-quarter	$\frac{1}{4}$	0.25	25%
One-third	$\frac{1}{3}$	0.333	$33\frac{1}{3}$%
One-half	$\frac{1}{2}$	0.5	50%
Two-thirds	$\frac{2}{3}$	0.667	$66\frac{2}{3}$%
One-fifth	$\frac{1}{5}$	0.2	20%

The parts of a fraction are called:

Denominator $\longrightarrow$ $\dfrac{3}{8}$ $\longleftarrow$ Numerator

Working with fractions

Fractions of quantities can be found by dividing the quantity by the bottom half of the fraction and then multiplying by the top half of the fraction. It doesn't matter whether you divide or multiply first (but in some other calculations the order does matter).

To find $\frac{3}{5}$ of 125.

    First $125 \div 5 = 25$
    then $25 \times 3 = 75$
    so $\frac{3}{5}$ of 125 is 75

Working with decimals

A decimal number uses the decimal point to separate the whole number (written on the left of the point) and the fractional part (written on the right of the point). Remember that a decimal with many digits needn't be a big number. For example, 22.4500 has 6 digits and 2245 has four digits, but 22.4500 is less than 2245.

Writing a number as a decimal needs thinking about. For example, there may be more **decimal places** than we need or more than is accurate. Calculators often churn out many more numbers than make sense. So we need to decide, or to be told, how many decimal places (dp) to use. To reduce the number of decimal places we need to round off.

3.862 becomes 3.86 when expressed to 2 dp (rounded downwards)
3.86 becomes 3.9 when expressed to 1 dp (rounded upwards)

You should indicate how many decimal places you have used for writing down a number. For example 3.86 (2 dp).

Working with percentages

Percent means 'out of a hundred' and if you were given a 4% wage increase then for every £100 you would get an extra £4. To work out the percentages of numbers other than 100, use the following formula.

> **To find the percentage of any number**
> number $\times$ percentage rate $\div 100$ = percentage (%)
>
> **To write a number as a percentage of another number**
> first number $\div$ second number $\times 100$ = percentage (%)

To find 7% of 600.
    Use   number $\times$ percentage rate $\div 100$ = percentage (%)
    so $600 \times 7 \div 100 = 42$

To express 42 as a percentage of 600.
    Use   (first number $\div$ second number) $\times 100$
    so $(42 \div 600) \times 100 = 7\%$

Remember that 10% is always the same as $\frac{1}{10}$ or dividing by 10. If a price ticket of £500 is increased by 10% then you need to find 10% of the original price and add it on:

10% of 500 = $\frac{1}{10}$ of 500 = 50

To add or subtract decimals
Place numbers in column; line up the decimal points; add or subtract as usual.
To multiply by 10
Move the decimal point to the right.
To divide by 10
Move the decimal point to the left.

dp is shorthand for decimal places.

For the rules of rounding up or down, see the **Useful Knowledge**, page 17.

So the new price is $500 + 50 = £550$. If the price were reduced by 10% then you would subtract the 10% ($500 - 50 = £450$).

> **Decimal method**
> - An alternative method of applying a percentage increase is to multiply the original by a factor. For 17.5% increase multiply by 1.175.
> - An alternative method of applying a percentage decrease is to multiply the original by a factor. For 10% decrease multiply by 0.9.

Reverse percentage

It is usually easier to be given the original amount and then calculate a percentage increase or decrease on that amount. But it is relatively common to be given the final figure with the percentage already applied. If you are asked for the *original* figure then you need to calculate in reverse.

The total price of a CD is £12 including VAT at 17.5%. What is the price of the CD before VAT?

$100\% + 17.5\% = 117.5\%$

117.5% is equivalent to £12

    1% is equivalent to $12 \div 117.5 \quad = £0.1021$

100% is equivalent to $0.1021 \times 100 = £10.21$

> **Decimal method**
> An alternative method is to divide the original by 1.175:
> $$£12 \div 1.175 = £10.21$$

Comparing numbers

Sometimes we wish to compare the sizes of two numbers. There is a choice methods, including fractions, percentages, proportions and ratios.

Ratio

We can compare any two numbers by writing them alongside one another separated by a ratio sign (:). For example, a cement/sand mixture of 1:3 tells us that for every one measure of cement there are three measures of sand. The usefulness of ratio is that we don't need to know whether the measure is a cup or a tank, as long as measure is the same size.

    We like ratios to be as simple as possible. The ratio 6:10 can be simplified because 6 and 10 have a common factor of 2. Dividing by 2 becomes 3:5. The trick is to divide both parts of the ratio by the *same* number so that the ratio remains true.

Ratios are often written with 1 as the first number. To achieve this then both numbers must be divided by the first number.

To simplify the ratio 3:5 and express is as 1:*x*.

Original ratio is	3:5
Divide each number by 3 to give	$1:1\frac{2}{3}$
Which can also be written as a decimal	1:1.67 (working to 2 dp)

Ratios can have more than two parts. For example, a recipe for a fruit drink says that apple juice, orange juice and lemonade are to be mixed in the ratio of 1:2:4. Which means:

1 part of apple juice : 2 parts of orange juice : 4 parts of lemonade

It doesn't matter what you use to measure a part as long as you keep it the same. And you must match the right number of parts to the right ingredient – 1 part of apple juice, 4 parts of orange juice and 2 parts of lemonade with produce a different drink.

Rule for ratios
Treat both parts of the ratio in the same way; always multiply both parts by the same number or divide both parts, by the same number.

Estimating

The way we write down a number gives information about the size of the number and also about the accuracy we are using. For example, to quote a cost as £6 million signals a different sort of accuracy to quoting the cost as £6 188 000.

Significant figures

The number 6 188 000 has 4 significant figures. If we round the number to the nearest million then the new number 6 000 000 has 1 significant figure. But notice that it is still a big number!

When we reduce the significant figures of a number, we use the rules of rounding – check the rules of rounding in the **Useful Knowledge** box – and then use zeros to show the correct size of the number. When dealing with decimal numbers we use similar rules. Look at the following examples.

sf means significant figures.

Number	Significant figures	Notes
569	3 sf	
569 000	3 sf	Ignore the zeros at the *end* of a number
569 732	6 sf	
4003	4 sf	The zeros within the number *do* count
400 300	4 sf	Ignore the zeros at the end of a number
0.569	3 sf	
0.569 732	6 sf	
0.005 69	3 sf	Ignore the zeros at the *front* of the number

Rough calculations

Rough calculations or estimates involve you working out figures in your head to give an approximate answer. You probably do this already.

You buy three cans of drink at 45p each: find the approximate cost.

45p is approximately	50p
3 times 50p is	150p

You do this in your head

So you expect the bill to be about £1.50. You would be surprised if you were asked to pay £13.50 instead of £1.35, the exact amount.

A simple rule for estimating is to round figures to 1sf. If the number is easy to deal with, like 25, then you might round to 2 sf. You need to be rather ruthless in keeping to the rule and not getting distracted by the smaller figures. Look at the following example.

Estimate the value for 235.8×19.

Simplify by rounding:	200×20 (using 1sf)
Multiply in your head:	4000

So the estimated answer can be stated: $235.8 \times 19 \approx 4000$

The wavy equals sign $\approx$ means that an answer is approximate.

USEFUL KNOWLEDGE

Digits or numerals
Digits are the symbols 0, 1, 2, 3, 4, 5, 6, 7, 8, 9. They are used in groups to make numbers such as 150, which is a number made of three digits

Multiples
A multiple of a number is that number multiplied by a whole number. The multiples of 3 are 6, 9, 12 ....

Factors
A factor is a number which divides exactly into another number. The factors of 12 are 1, 2, 3, 4, 6.

Prime
A prime number is a number having only two factors, 1 and itself. Examples are 2, 3, 5, 7, 11, 13, 17, 19, 23, etc.

Index form
Index form uses a small number (superscript) on another number, usually 10; for example, $10^2 = 10 \times 10 = 100$.

Adding and subtracting negative numbers
Draw a number line; for positive (+) numbers move to the right and for negative (−) numbers move to the left.

Fractions
Fractions can be written with a horizontal line or a slanting line. One-third can be written $\frac{1}{3}$ (horizontal line) or ⅓ (slanting line). The numerator is the number above the horizontal line (on the left of the slanting line) and the denominator is the number below the horizontal line (on the right of the slanting line).

Rules of rounding

Find the last digit of your number then find the next digit to the right. If this digit is 1 to 4, discard it and leave the last digit unchanged. If it is 5 or above, discard it but increase the last digit by 1.

Percentages

To find the percentage of any number, use this formula:

number × percentage rate ÷ 100 = percentage (%)

To find 22% of 400 calculate 400 × 22 ÷ 100 = 5%.

Data

A set of data is a collection of measurements, or other numbers, which are often obtained by carrying out a statistical survey. Data can be shown in a variety of ways, including the graphs and charts in previous chapters. Data can be divided into two types:

The word **data** can be used as plural and the word **datum** used as singular. But in modern statistics and computing it is alright to use the word **data** as singular and to write **the data is**.

- **Discrete data** is obtained by counting and can only have fixed numbers. For example, the number of cars passing a point. There are no fractions.
- **Continuous data** can be any size of number within agreed rules. For example, the figures for heights of people or weights of people.

Average values and spread

A set of data is a list of numbers, perhaps many hundreds of numbers, and we don't usually present this raw information. We need to summarise the effect of the data by using just a few numbers. The idea of an average value is to use just *one* number to give people a feeling for the centre of all the numbers in the data, such as the ages of people in a town.

However, a simple average value by itself may give you a wrong idea about the total effect of the data. Look at data sets A and B. Both sets of data have the same average or central figure of 20, but they have different spreads or range. Data set A has a smaller or tighter spread of 4; data set B has a larger or more spread out range of 24.

Data set A (ages):	**18**	**20**	**22**		*Data set B (ages)*:	**8**	**20**	**32**
Average = 20					Average = 20			
Range = 4 (22 − 18)					Range = 24 (32 − 8)			

To give a better summary of data we have a choice of methods, including a choice of 'average'. A simple average is called a **mean** and there are additional ideas of **median** and **mode** which help describe the shape of the data. It is best to start using these statistical words accurately and you can look at the **Useful Knowledge** box to check the definitions when you need to.

Mean (average)

Mean is the most common type of average value. Here is a set of 11 numbers:

5	4	8	3	3	4	6	7	6	4	12

To calculate the mean, all the data is added up and the total divided by the number of items:

$$\text{Mean} = \frac{(5 + 4 + 8 + 3 + 3 + 4 + 6 + 7 + 6 + 4 + 12)}{11} = \frac{62}{11} = 5.6$$

The symbol for mean is x.

Range

The simple example of ages on page 18 shows how two sets of numbers which have the same value for mean can be rather different in other ways. The range tells us the difference between the highest and the lowest values and is a simple indication that the spread is different.

Returning to the set of 11 numbers.

5	4	8	3	3	4	6	7	6	4	12

The range is found by inspecting the numbers to find the lowest (which is 3) and the highest (which is 12). The value of the range is then $12 - 3 = 9$.

Mean is the central average value.
Median is the middle value.
Mode is the most popular value.
Range is the gap between smallest and largest.

Median and mode

To find the median you need to arrange the data in order from smallest to largest, then select the middle number. Let's use our set of 11 numbers:

5	4	8	3	3	4	6	7	6	4	12

Rearranging the numbers in order we get

3	3	4	4	4	5	6	6	7	8	12

To find the median you identify the number in the middle of the data set. It has the same number of items above it and below it. You can find the median by just looking and counting, but don't worry about the size of the numbers. Here, the median is 5, because there are as many values above as below:

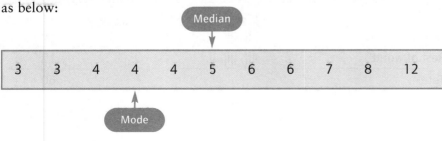

To find the mode you identify the value in the data set which occurs most often – it is the most popular number. Once again, this is done by eye and the answer is 4, because 4 occurs 3 times in the line-up.

> **Take care!** When rearranging the order of data from smallest to largest don't lose any entries.

Collecting data

We often collect information by reading the scales on instruments or by observing and counting events. In all cases it is best to record this data on questionnaires or tables that you have prepared in advance. To survey the travel destinations of a large group of people, the following table needs to be drawn up in advance. Otherwise you will be trying to write down places and numbers and continually changing them.

Destination	Tally	Frequency
England		
Ireland		
Scotland		
Wales		
Rest of Europe		
Rest of world		
Total		

The **tally** is used by making one stroke for each item (destination) counted. The fifth stroke is drawn as a diagonal 'gate'; it stands for an item and it helps the eye count the strokes at a later stage. The **frequency** is the total number of times that a particular group (destination) occurs.

Destination	Tally	Frequency
England	ℍℍ ℍℍ ℍℍ ℍℍ	20
Ireland	‖‖‖	4
Scotland	ℍℍ ‖	6
Wales	‖	2
Rest of Europe	ℍℍ ℍℍ ℍℍ ‖	16
Rest of world	ℍℍ ℍℍ ‖‖	12
Total		60

Grouping data

Counting travel destinations is an example of **discrete** data, which is always in whole numbers. Other data, such as ages of people or salaries paid, is **continuous** and can be any number. But for statistics we need to group the data. The data in the following table is part of a questionnaire enquiring about people's ages and salaries. Notice that the person designing the questionnaire has chosen the groups and decided the boundaries for the ages and the salaries.

Age in years	Less than 15 years	15–24	25–34	35–44	45–54	55–64	65 and above
Salary in £000	up to 10	10–19	20–29	30–39	40–49	50–59	60 and over

USEFUL KNOWLEDGE

Range
For a set of data, the range is the difference between the smallest and the largest number in that data.

Mean or arithmetic mean
Mean is a measure of central tendency. It is found by adding together all numbers in the data and dividing by how many numbers there are.

Median
For a set of data arranged in order of size, the median is the value in the middle of the set. For example, 7 is the median of 4, 4, 7, 9, 11.

Mode
The mode of a set of data is the value that is found most often. For example, 4 is the mode of 4, 4, 7, 9, 11.

Discrete data
Discrete data is obtained by counting and can only have fixed numbers. For example, the number of cars passing a point. There are no fractions.

Continuous data
Continuous data can be any size of number within agreed rules. For example, the figures for heights of people or weights of people can be any number, so we usually need to group them.

Correlation
Correlation is the strength of connection between two sets of data. It can be strong, weak, or non-existent:
- Strong correlation: points make a reasonable straight line on a scattergram.
- Weak correlation: points are all over the place on a scattergram.

Measuring and observing

This chapter deals with ways of getting information by using equipment such as a watch or a thermometer. These instruments are used to **measure** how much we have of a **quantity** such as time or temperature. You can also obtain information about quantities by reading maps and technical drawings which have been drawn to scale.

Measuring systems

To measure a quantity such as time or length we have to agree upon a system of units. For example, seconds, minutes and hours is the system used by everyone to measure time. But for other measurements there has been a choice, such as metres or feet, degrees Celsius or degrees Fahrenheit.

The metric system, which uses units such as metres, grams and litres, is the official system of measurement in most countries. The metric system is also used for science and technology in all countries and is called the **SI system**. The **Imperial system**, which uses units such as feet, pounds weight and gallons, is also in common use in the UK and the USA. Other sections of this book show you how to change between units, such as from degrees Celsius to degrees Fahrenheit.

Symbols

There is an official system of shorthand for writing units and these symbols are listed on page 23. Look at the following examples:

21 °C	means that the temperature is 21 degrees Celsius
1200 g	means that the mass is 1200 grams (sometimes grammes)
1.2 kg	means that the mass is 1.2 kilograms
3000 mm	means that the length is 3000 millimetres
3 m	means that the length is 3 metres

Large and small units

When the size of numbers in measurements gets large or small, we make the unit larger or smaller by putting a **prefix** in front of the unit. For

---

Typical measurements
time
length
mass
volume
temperature

Some metric units
millimetre, metre, kilometre (for length)
gram, kilogram (for mass)
litre, cubic metre (for volume)
degree Celsius (for temperature)

Some imperial units
inch, foot (for length)
ounce, pound, stone (for mass)
pint, gallon, cubic feet (for volume)
degree Fahrenheit (for temperature)

example kilo always means a thousand (1000) and milli always means one thousandth (1/1000):

2 000 000 mm   is the same as 2000 m
2 000 m   is the same as 2 km
2 km   is the same as 2 000 000 mm

The example shows how 2 kilometres can be written in at least three different ways. Although they all mean the same thing, we are more comfortable when handling smaller numbers. Therefore the general rule is that when there are more than four figures it is time to convert by using another prefix. So 2 000 000 mm needs converting to either 2000 m or 2 km. Other prefixes are listed on page 24.

1 kilovolt   = 1 kV   = 1000 V
1 millimetre   = 1 mm   = 0.001 m
1 nanosecond   = 1 ns   = 0.000 000 001 s

Quantity	Symbol	Unit	Symbol
Some SI base units			
Length	l	metre	m
Mass	m	kilogram	kg
Time	t	second	s
Some other SI units			
Area	A	square metre	m^2
Volume	V	cubic metre	m^3
Velocity	v	metre per second	m/s
Force	F	newton	N
Energy	E	joule	J
Power	P	watt	W
Pressure	p	pascal	Pa
Some other units in common use			
Velocity or speed	v	kilometres per hour	kph
Concentration	c	parts per million	ppm
Pressure	p	pounds per square inch	psi

Prefix	Symbol	Multiply by
tera	T	$\times 10^{12}$ or 1 000 000 000 000
giga	G	$\times 10^{9}$ or 1 000 000 000
mega	M	$\times 10^{6}$ or 1 000 000
kilo	k	$\times 10^{3}$ or 1 000
		$\times 1$
centi	c	$\times 10^{-2}$ or 0.01
milli	m	$\times 10^{-3}$ or 0.001
micro	μ	$\times 10^{-6}$ or 0.000 001
nano-	n	$\times 10^{-9}$ or 0.000 000 001
pico	p	$\times 10^{-12}$ or 0.000 000 000 001

Notes
Centi is a non-standard prefix but remains because it is convenient.
Notice that M and m have different meanings.
The symbol μ is the Greek letter called mu.

Reading scales

In most practical situations you use a ruler for measuring length, a set of scales for weighing mass, a thermometer for temperature and so on. The scale that you read may be in a straight line or it may be a circular dial – the effect is the same.

When we look at the time on a clock face or measure with a ruler we often have to read *between* the markings and then decide what number it is and what units are being used. With a clock you have had many years of practice at judging where the hand is, and you know the units are hours and minutes. With some other measurements you need to take a little more care when reading the scale.

There are three points on the kitchen scales in the figure, marked A, B and C. To get a reading you need to use your eye to check the distance to the nearest marking on the scale. You then need to think about what number of grams that is. The scale is only marked every 100 g but there are five equal spaces between the markings. So each mark without a number is $\frac{1}{5}$ of 100 g, which is 20 g.

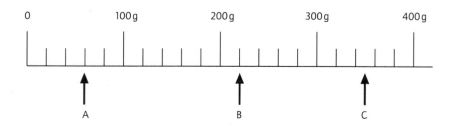

Point	Reading	Working
A	60 g	Each marking is 20 g. Reading is 3 markings above 0. So add 3 × 20 g to 0, giving 60 g
B	220 g	Each marking is 20 g. Reading is 1 marking above 200 g. So add 1 × 20 g to 200 g, giving 220 g
C	350 g	Each marking is 20 g and this reading is halfway between 40 g and 60 g, i.e. 50 g. Then add 50 g to 300 g, giving 350 g

Maps and scales

When we make a map, a technical drawing or a model, it has to be smaller than the real thing otherwise we would need a piece of paper as big as the UK to make a map of the UK! But the reduction in size needs to have a fixed ratio or proportion which is called the **scale** of the map or drawing.

Example	Typical scale	Note
Road map	1:500 000	1 cm on map is 500 000 cm of road (5000 m)
Technical drawing of a building	1:100	1 cm on drawing is 100 cm (1 m) in building
Large model of a boat	1:20	1 in on model is 20 in of real boat

See also: **Ratio**, page 14.

Using maps

The scale of a map is marked somewhere on the map. It can be shown in the following ways:

A maths ratio   1:200 000
Metric units   2 km to 1 cm
Imperial units   3.2 miles to 1 inch
Measuring scale   A line in one corner of the map with marks to show typical real-world distances.

Here is an example of a measuring scale:
To use a map to find the distance in the real world:

- Measure a distance on the map.
- Use the scale to convert map distance to real distance.
- Add units for the real distance.
- Check that the result is sensible.

Roads on a map don't usually run in straight lines between places. So to measure a distance on the map you might use some cotton or string.

If a map has a scale of 3.2 miles to 1 inch, then:

$\frac{1}{2}$ inch on the map will be $\frac{1}{2}$ × 3.2 = 1.6 real miles
2 inches on the map will be 2 × 3.2 = 6.4 real miles

Using drawings

The scale of a technical drawing is marked somewhere on the drawing. It is usually shownas a maths ratio, e.g. 1:100, or as dimension lines. Dimension lines are lines with arrowheads to show the real-life distance between major points.

USEFUL KNOWLEDGE

SI metric units

The SI system is the official system of metric units based on the metre (m) for length, the kilogram (kg) for mass, and the second (s) for time.

1 cm = 10 mm	1 m = 100 cm	1 km = 1000 m
1 kg = 1000 g	1 tonne = 1000 kg	
1 litre = 1000 ml	1 litre = 1000 cm^3	1 cm^3 = 1 ml

Imperial units

Imperial units are based on the foot for length, the pound for mass, and the second for time. These systems are used in the UK and the USA and for some units, such as the gallon and the ton, the sizes are slightly different between the UK and the USA.

1 foot = 12 inches	1 yard = 3 feet
1 pound = 16 Ounces (Oz)	1 stone = 14 pounds (lb)
1 gallon = 8 pints	

Prefixes

A prefix is a group of letters in front of a word which modifies the meaning of the word. In the SI system, the prefix 'kilo' means multiply by 1000; examples are kilometre and kilovolt. See the table of SI units.

Rules for writing SI units

- Only one prefix can be used, so kilokilovolt becomes megavolt.
- Numbers are expressed in groups of three; they are separated by spaces not by commas, e.g. 3 000 000.
- Units start with a lower case letter when written in full but their abbreviations begin with a capital letter. The newton (N) is the unit for measuring force and the pascal (Pa) is the unit for measuring pressure.

Rules for using scales

- Measure a distance on the map or drawing.
- Use the scale to convert paper distance to real distance.
- Add units for the real distance.
- Check that the result is sensible.

Calculations

The aim of doing calculations is to get answers that are useful in your life, not to learn about mathematics. But even when using electronic calculators we need to know some rules of calculation given in this chapter. It then leads on to the idea of using formulas for doing calculations.

Remember 'gigo':
Garbage in, garbage out.

Calculators

Simple electronic calculators are found everywhere and we can use them to do the hard boring crunch of calculations. But *you* still need to do the thinking because the calculator does exactly what it is told, for good or bad. For example, did we enter the correct numbers and does the final answer seem sensible? Here are the stages of using a calculator:

Calculator operations

Operations are what a calculator does with numbers when you press the instruction keys or command keys. The ADD key, usually labelled with a + sign, is an example of an operation key. This table lists a selection of calculator operations.

Operation	Button	Effect
Addition	+	Adds
Subtraction	−	Subtracts (takes away)
Multiplication	×	Multiplies (times)
Division	÷	Divides
Clear	C/CE or CLR	Clears display and clears memories
Memory in +	M+	Stores number and/or adds it to anything in memory
Memory in −	M−	Stores number and/or subtracts it from anything in memory
Memory out	MR or RCL	Recalls number from memory and onto display, where it can be used
Square root	√	Works out square root
Percentage	%	Adds or subtracts a percentage change

For a definition of square root, *see* **Useful Knowledge**, page 34.

When using a calculator you still need to think about the answer, especially when the calculator gives a more accurate answer than is sensible. You need to decide how many decimal places you need and then use the rules of rounding.

Use a calculator to divide 20 by 3.
Press the following keys

and the display will show

Common errors with calculators
Not clearing old numbers on screen.
Entering wrong numbers.
Not pressing [=] at the end.

Because of the repeating number, this answer is being quoted to many decimal places. Yet the input numbers were not that accurate and it is misleading to quote all the numbers. Instead the answer could be quoted as 6.67 (2 dp).

> **Note** A computer keyboard has a calculator keypad. The key for multiply is often marked with a *. The symbols * and x mean the same thing – multiply. They key for divide is often marked with the /. The symbols / and ÷ mean the same thing – divide.

Advanced calculators

Some advanced calculator buttons
[(for brackets
EXP or EE for standard form
$a\frac{b}{c}$ for fractions
x^y for powers

See also: **Large and small numbers**, page 11.

Calculators come in various types; they include simple calculators, scientific calculators, programmable calculators and graphics calculators. Even simple calculators can calculate a square root and most calculations can be carried out with a simple calculator like the one illustrated. If you do have a more advanced model, make sure you don't get confused by the extra keys. Learn to use them by reading the instructions.

An important feature of all advanced calculators is the ability to handle very large and very small numbers. The calculator does this by using the **standard form**, also called **scientific notation**. The calculator button for standard form is EXP or EE and it automatically adds the power of 10 ($\times 10^n$).

Multiply 4 000 000 by 2 000 000 000.
Written in standard form these numbers are 4×10^6 and 2×10^9, and most calculators will use the following sequence of entries:

Depending on your type of calculator the display will show:

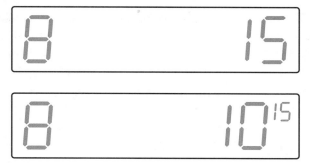

Both displays mean 8×10^{15}. It is always up to you to read your calculator screen and to correctly interpret the display.

> **Take care!** Do not press $\times 10$ as well as EXP, because EXP already contains the idea of $\times 10$.

Checking calculations

All calculations are a waste of time if you get results which don't make sense or have no use. Use the following questions and checks to help you get meaningful results.

Check	Examples
Is the input data correct?	Read the instrument correctly Check the scales and units Copy or write the numbers down correctly
Is the formula correct?	Choose the right formula Write it down correctly Put the right figures in the formula
Have I used the calculator correctly?	Use the correct keys Copy correctly from the screen
Can I get the same result twice?	Repeat the above stages
Does the result agree with an estimated result?	Estimate by rounding the figures to 1 or 2 significant figures and do a simple sum
Is the accuracy suitable?	The calculator may read 21.472 38 but you only need 4 significant figures
Do I need to use units?	The final answer might be in metres or degrees

BODMAS

There is a rule that gives the correct order for doing all calculations and for writing down formulas. The strange-sounding word BODMAS is made up from letters of the following operations starting with B for brackets:

First do	**Brackets**	so 4 + (3 × 2) is 4 + 6
Then do	**Other** (or power)	such as 3^2 or$\sqrt{4}$
Then do	**Divide** or	
	Multiply	
Then do	**Add** or	
	Subtract	

If there are no brackets, or powers, then just move to the next operation in the list. It doesn't actually matter in which order you divide or multiply as they have equal priority but both of them have a higher priority than add and subtract.

Conversions

In an earlier section of the book we used a graph to convert between the temperature units of degrees Celsius and degrees Fahrenheit. But if you don't have a graph, you can use a a formula. The simplest type of formula is to multiply by a **conversion factor** such as those listed in the table.

Imperial units into metric units			Metric units to imperial units		
To convert	into	multiply by	To convert	into	multiply by
inches	centimetres	2.5	centimetres	inches	0.39
feet	metres	0.30	metres	feet	3.3
yards	metres	0.91	metres	yards	1.1
miles	kilometres	1.6	kilometres	miles	0.62
sq yards	sq metres	0.84	sq metres	sq yards	1.2
acres	hectares	0.40	hectares	acres	2.5
cubic feet	cubic metres	0.028	cubic metres	cubic feet	35
gallons	litres	4.5	litres	gallons	0.22
pounds	kilograms	0.45	kilograms	pounds	2.2
ounces	grams	28	grams	ounces	0.04

The conversion factors are given to 2 significant figures.

Conversion factors are numbers used to multiply one unit to convert it to an equivalent amount in another unit. The units might be measurements such as length; the conversion factor never changes. Or the units might be for money, in which case you have to look up the latest exchange rate. Here is an example:

Convert a length of 8 inches to centimetres; work to 2 significant figures.

Steps	Working
Write down inches	8 inches
Look up table of conversion factors	*multiply inches by 2.5*
Calculate	$8 \times 2.5 = 20$
Interpret result	8 in converts to 20 cm (2 sf)

Formulas

Formulas are instructions on how to carry out calculations and they are written in a shorthand. For example, the formula for the area of a rectangle is written:

$$A = lw$$

It means multiply the length by the breadth. The numbers you multiply depend upon the size of your particular rectangle, such as a room, but this **general formula** works for any length or width. Using letters to stand in for numbers is called **algebra** and its ideas can become very powerful. For key skills we only need to use the shorthand of algebra in order to get results.

Using formulas

To use a general formula like those for areas and volumes you need to have certain measurements available, such as the length and width of a room. The method of putting real numbers into a formula is called **substitution**. Just like substituting players in a football team, the aim is keep the same balance in the formula.

The formula to calculate the volume of a cylinder, $A = lb$, uses only two **variables** (things that can change) and only one **operation** (multiply). But some formulas contain rather more variables and have a sequence of operations. Always follow BODMAS when creating or using a formula. Here is an example.

Shorthand in formulas

lw means $l \times w$
d/t or d/t means $d \div t$
r^2 means $r \times r$

A cylindrical container is measured and found to be 10 cm in diameter and 20 cm in height. The following steps of working show how to calculate the volume of the room using the formula $V = \pi r^2 h$.

Steps	Working
Interpret the information Use symbols and numbers to write down what you know and don't know	$V = ?$ $h = 20$ cm $r = 10 \div 2 = 5$ cm (radius is half the diameter) $\pi = 3.14$ (2 dp)
Write down the formula	$V = \pi \times r^2 \times h$ $V = \pi r^2 h$ if you omit $\times$
Substitute what you know into the formula	$V = 3.14 \times 5^2 \times 20$
Calculate in correct order starting with the power (BODMAS rule)	$V = 3.14 \times 25 \times 20$ $V = 1570$
Interpret and present the results Put the answer back into real words and add units.	Volume is 1570 cm^3

Formulae is an alternative spelling for formulas.

The figure opposite gives formulas for the areas, volumes and other dimensions of common shapes. Using some of these formulas can get tricky and you are best to write out all lines of working, as above. Further examples are given in the table.

Formula	Used for	Notes
$V = IR$	Voltage (V) when given the electric current (I) and the resistance (R)	This is the formula which results from Ohm's law in science
$I = \dfrac{PR}{100}$	Simple interest (I) for one year, where P is the loan (principal) and R is the interest rate	Calculate in any order
$A = \pi r^2$	Area of a circle, where r is the radius	First: calculate the square of r (BODMAS) then multiply by the constant π
$A = 2\pi(r + h)$	Total surface area of a cylinder, where r is the radius and h is the height	First calculate $(r + h)$ then multiply by 2π
$C = \frac{5}{9}(F - 32)$	To convert degrees Fahrenheit (F) to degrees Celsius (C)	First calculate $(F - 32)$ then multiply by $\frac{5}{9}$
$c^2 = a^2 + b^2$ $c = \sqrt{a^2 + b^2}$	To find the length of the long side (c) of a right-angled triangle (Pythagoras)	First calculate $a^2 + b^2$ then take the long bar of the square root sign acts as a bracket
$FV = P\left(1 + \dfrac{R}{100}\right)^N$	Effect of compound interest. Final value (FV) for principal (P), interest rate (R) and number of years (N)	First calculate $(1 + R/100)$ then raise it to the power of N and multiply by P

Rectangle

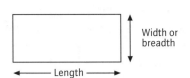

Area = length × width
Perimeter = 2 × (length + width)

Parallelogram

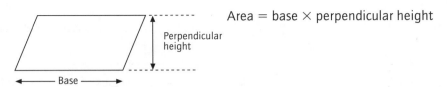

Area = base × perpendicular height

Trapezium

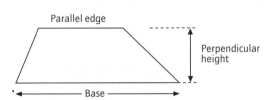

Area = $\frac{1}{2}$ × (base + parallel edge)
× perpendicular height

Triangle

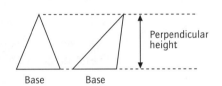

Area = $\frac{1}{2}$ × base × perpendicular height

Circle

Area = π × radius × radius = πr^2 or $\frac{1}{4}\pi d^2$
Circumference = 2 × π × radius
= π × diameter = πd

Arc of a circle

Length of arc = $\dfrac{\text{Angle (in degrees) of arc at centre}}{360}$ × circumference of full circle

$= \dfrac{\theta°}{360°} = 2\pi r^2$

Section of a circle

Area of sector = angle (in degrees) of sector at centre × area of full circle

$= \dfrac{\theta°}{360°} \times \pi r^2$

Ellipse

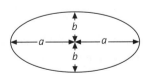

Area of ellipse = πab
Circumference = $\pi(a + b)$ (first approximation)
or $\pi[3(a + b) - \sqrt{(a + 3b)(3a + b)}]$
(better approximation)

Cylinder

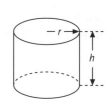

Volume = π × radius × radius × height = $\pi r^2 h$
Curved surface area = 2 × π × radius × height
$\qquad\qquad\qquad\qquad = 2\pi rh$
Total surface area $\quad = 2\pi r\,(r + h)$

Cone

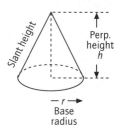

Slant height
Perp. height h
r
Base radius

Volume = $\frac{1}{3}$ × area of base × perpendicular height
$\qquad\quad = \frac{1}{3}\pi r^2 h$
Curved surface area
$\qquad\quad = \pi$ × radius of base × slant height
Slant height = $\sqrt{r^2 + h^2}$

Sphere

Volume = $\frac{3}{4}$ × π × (radius)^3 = $\frac{1}{6}\pi$ × (diameter)^3
Surface area = 4 × π × (radius)^2 = π × (diameter)^2

Pyramid

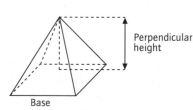

Perpendicular height
Base

Volume = $\frac{1}{3}$ × area of base × perpendicular height

Frustrum

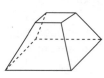

Volume = $\frac{1}{3}$ × (A + B + $\sqrt{AB}$) × h
where A and B are the areas of the top and bottom parallel faces and h is the perpendicular distance between them

Rearranging formulas

We sometimes need to move the parts of a formula around to give us the answer we want. For example, the formula for velocity (*v*) is distance (*d*) divided by time taken (*t*) and it is written:

$v = \dfrac{d}{t}$

But if you want to find the distance (d) then it is convenient to change the formula around to make d the subject of the formula:

d = v × t

This rearrangement of the formula also called transposition, must follow a system of rules so that the formula still remains true. Here are the main rules for changing the subject of a formula.

Guide	Examples
The aim is to have the subject of the formula on the left side of the equals sign, without any attachments	$r = D/2$ not $2r = D$
When a part is moved from one side of the equals sign to the other, it has the *opposite* effect. Adding becomes subtracting, multiplying becomes dividing	$v = u + 2t$ can become $v - u = 2t$ or $v - 2t = u$ $V = IR$ can become $V/R = I$ or $V/I = R$
A part can be moved from one side to the other as long as it affects *all* the rest of the parts	In the formula $A = 2\pi$ $(r + h)$ the r + h must be kept together if moved

Transposing a formula is to rearrange it to produce an equivalent version.

The formula for converting Fahrenheit temperature (F) to Celsius temperature (C) is $C = \frac{5}{9}(F - 32)$. Rearrange this formula to convert Celsius temperature to Fahrenheit temperature (make F the subject).

Steps	Working
Move the 5 to the opposite side, where it divides Move the 9 to the other side, where it multiplies	$C = \frac{5}{9}(F - 32)$ $\frac{9}{5}C = (F - 32)$
Remove brackets as they no longer do anything Move the 32 to the opposite side, where it adds	$\frac{9}{5}C + 32 = F$
Swap the sides of the equation, because we normally expect the subject to be by itself on the left	$F = \frac{9}{5}C + 32$

USEFUL KNOWLEDGE

Square

To square a number is to multiply that number by itself.
Symbol: N^2 where N is the number you are squaring
Example: 4^2 means work out $4 \times 4 = 16$

Square root

When you multiply a number by itself you obtain a square – 16 is the square of 4.
The number that you multiplied by itself is the square root – 4 is the square root of 16.
Symbol: $\sqrt{N}$ where N is the number you are taking the square root of
Example: $\sqrt{36} = 6$ (because $6 \times 6 = 36$)

BODMAS rule

Brackets first then **O**ther (such as powers), then **D**ivide and **M**ultiply, then **A**dd and **S**ubtract

Algebra

The branch of maths which deals with calculations by using general letters or symbols to represent numbers.

Shorthand in formulas

ab means a multiplied by b
a/b or $\frac{a}{b}$ means a divided by b

MONEY MATTERS

Interest Extra money paid in return for having the use of someone else's money (called the principal). The rate is usually expressed as a percentage for a year.

Simple interest Interest calculated by keeping the principal (P) unchanged for each period.

Formula: $I = \dfrac{PR}{100}$ for interest rate R

Compound interest Interest calculated by taking the interest earned at the end of each period (N) and adding it to the principal (P).

Formula: $FV = P\left(\dfrac{1+R}{100}\right)^N$ for interest rate R

Annual percentage rate (APR) A standard way of calculating and showing the interest for loans, so that different offers can be compared.

Gross The total amount of money *before* any deductions are made, such as for tax.

Net The amount of money remaining *after* any deductions are made.

Areas and volumes

Mensuration is the word used in some books for area and volume calculations.

A common application is to calculate areas and volumes. Whether you have to pay for it, or paint it, you will first need to calculate it. The figure on page 33 shows some simple shapes and gives the formulas for their area and volume.

Calculating with triangles

If you need a reminder of the basic facts about triangles, see the box on the next page. To calculate the area of a triangle the following formula is relatively simple:

$$A = \tfrac{1}{2} b \times h$$

But to get the base (b) or the height (h) of a triangle you may first need to use the formula of Pythagoras.

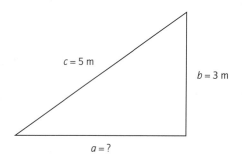

$c = 5\text{ m}$

$b = 3\text{ m}$

$a = ?$

Find the length of the missing side in this triangle.

Steps	Working
Write down what you know and the formula to use	$a = ?$ $b = 3$ $c = 5$ $a^2 + b^2 = c^2$
Substitute the numbers into the formula	$a^2 + 3^2 = 5^2$
First calculate the squares (BODMAS rule)	$a^2 + 9 = 25$
Rearrange the equation and simplify	$a^2 = 25 - 9$ $a^2 = 16$
Take the square root of each side Calculate the square root	$a = 16$ $a = 4$
Interpret the answer and check it is sensible	*Length of missing side is* 4 cm

Composite areas and volumes

To calculate the areas or volumes of many shapes in real life, you need to split them into simpler shapes. For example, to calculate the volume of a swimming pool with the shape shown in the diagram, you need to split it into rectangle A and triangle B.

A **composite** or **compound shape** is made up of two of more simple shapes.

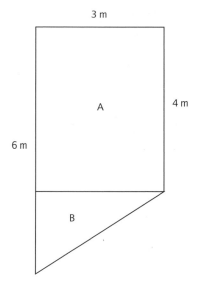

KNOW YOUR TRIANGLES

Triangle A shape with three sides; the sides must be straight lines.

Angles inside triangle The angles inside any triangle add up to total of 180°.

Equilateral triangle A triangle that has three sides of equal length; this means that all three corners have an angle of 60°.

Isosceles triangle A triangle that has two sides the same length.

Right-angled triangle A triangle where one angle is 90°.

Hypotenuse The longest side of a right-angled triangle; this side is always opposite the right angle.

Opposite In a right-angled triangle it is the side which is opposite the angle being considered.

Adjacent In a right-angled triangle it is the side next to the angle being considered and also next to the right angle.

Pythagoras' theorem In a right-angled triangle, the squares of the two smaller sides add up to the same value as the square of the longest side (the hypotenuse):

$$a^2 + b^2 = c^2$$

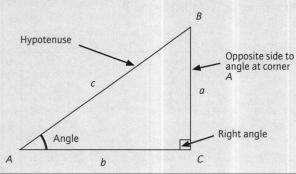

Part 2: The Bottom Line

This part concentrates on what you must do to get your key skills qualification. It will show you:

- The words and ideas of the key skills.
- The definition of level 3.
- How you can practise the skills.
- What must be in your portfolio of evidence.

This part is divided into three sections:

- **What the unit expects:** This section will explain the evidence requirements of the number key skill, and how to put your portfolio together. Your portfolio is the key to getting your key skill – this part of the book tells you how to choose your evidence and get it ready.
- **Evidence for level 3**
- **Other forms of assessment and evidence:** This section will tell you about the external assessment and how to prepare for it.

Qualifications and Curriculum Authority

The key skills specifications are published by the QCA, and are widely available through schools, colleges, training establishments and awarding bodies. They are also available on the QCA website (www.qca.org.uk).

What the unit expects

What is level 3 all about

Evidence is the proof that you can do what is required in order to get the key skills. It is proof that you have learned about number and that you can use and apply what you have learned.

At level 3 you will see that there are basically three types of **evidence** that you need to provide. The key skills unit at level 1 ask you to show that you can apply your number skills and provide evidence for the following three areas:

- Planning an activity and interpreting information
- Carrying out calculations
- Interpreting results and presenting findings.

You can collect the evidence for each of the three areas from different places if you like. For example, one module or unit from an A-level or Vocational A-level or another qualification might be great for showing that you can interpret information but might not be much use at helping you collect evidence to show you can carry out calculations. Another opportunity might exist for only carrying out calculations and nothing else. At level 3 this doesn't matter and, whenever you can, you should make use of your best opportunities for collecting evidence.

What's your point?

It is not enough to just interpret or present information that uses numbers. You have to be doing it for a reason. You need to have a **purpose** for using the numbers you collect. The number key skills will keep asking you to use the numerical information for a purpose and you will need to provide evidence that you have a purpose in mind and you can use the information effectively to meet it. For example, finding out when the next train leaves, wanting to find out how much you have in the bank, trying to find out how much carpet to buy or even using a thermometer to find out the temperature, all are reasons or purposes for using numbers.

SOURCES THAT USE NUMBERS

At level 3 you need to show you can use at least two different sources of information. At some point you will have to show you can use a large data set as one of the sources of information.

- Tables (currency, temperature)
- Diagrams
- Charts
- Graphs
- Thermometers
- Scales
- Other measuring instruments, e.g.: micrometer, voltmeter
- Electricity and/or gas meters
- Maps
- Bank statements
- Bills
- Payslips
- Scale drawings
- Schematic diagrams
- Floor plans and building drawings
- Examples of large data sets (at least 50 items):
  Spreadsheets
  Computer data printouts

What about your portfolio?

Building your portfolio of Application of Number evidence

Your portfolio of evidence is the work that you have done that will prove to your teacher and others that you can do what the key skills ask you to do. It is the proof you will need to get the key skills award.

A key skills unit is quite a large chunk of work. It is roughly the same size as a Vocational A-level unit or an A-level module. So you may have to carry out a number of different tasks to have sufficient evidence to show you can meet the key skills requirements. Make sure your portfolio is well organised and that the work inside is clear and easily understood.

The simplest approach to collecting and keeping your evidence is to have a separate folder or portfolio for your number evidence. This is by far the easiest way to organise your work and keep a record of what you have done and what there is still to do. Consider using the following handy references as a way of organising and labelling your work:

- Have a contents page that you keep updating as you build up your evidence.

- Keep records of when you collected your evidence and where it came from (e.g. which A-level module or unit).
- Get into the habit of writing down the purpose for your work as you collect evidence.
- Use the Key skills sections (interpreting information, calculating and presenting your findings) as sections dividing up your portfolio.
- Copies of work are acceptable if the actual key skills evidence is part of another course; the original work can be kept with the course that it comes from.
- Keep a checklist of all the things that you must cover in your portfolio (in the presenting section you must show you can use one chart and one diagram).

Evidence for level 3

Information

At level 3 you will need to show that you can look at a range of different sources and take from them relevant information to help you fulfil your purpose. This can involve secondary sources with both written and graphical material but you must also learn how to generate your own information by using primary sources, creating the information first-hand. Taking measurements, carrying out surveys or making observations are possible ways to create information for yourself.

Calculations

At level 3 you need to show that you can carry out multi-step calculations. This means that there are several steps to calculate or work out before you get the answer. This is a way of ensuring that the calculations you make at level 3 are not too easy. If you are calculating the volume of a sphere that has a radius of 3 cm, using the formula $\frac{4}{3}\pi r^3$, then the steps will look like this:

- **Step 1** substitute in the values using 3.14, which is π to 2 decimal places:

$$\frac{4 \times 3.14 \times 3^3}{3}$$

- **Step 2**: calculate 3^3 then multiply the top line:

$$\frac{4 \times 3.14 \times 27}{3}$$

- **Step 3**: now divide by 3:

$$\frac{339.12}{3}$$

- **Answer**: the volume of the sphere is: $113.04\,\text{cm}^3$

Take care! One more key feature of the level 3 number requirements is that you have to do at least one task that involves interpreting information, carrying out calculations and interpreting results and presenting your findings, all as part of the same task. You must do at least one task, you could do more. This is what the key skills requirements mean when they ask for one **substantial and complex** activity. This is a level 3 requirement.

This is also to show that you are able to plan larger and more difficult tasks by breaking them down into a logical series of smaller tasks. This means that one of your reasons or purposes to interpret, calculate and present results

---

will have to be big enough to help you do this larger and more complex activity. Many of the signposts in Part 3 of the book highlight potential activities that are complex enough to help you meet this requirement.

You can address each of the three areas individually to collect the rest of the evidence; you can carry out different tasks for each; or you can put together evidence that involves two of the areas together, if this is appropriate. Because of the amount of evidence you will need to produce you will probably use all three ways of generating evidence.

Planning an activity and interpreting information

What you must learn to do

This part of the key skills is basically asking you to show that you can focus on activities that involve using numbers, planning how to tackle them and getting the information you need.

It is asking you to show you can work with large numbers, small numbers, numbers that appear on charts, tables, graphs or in drawings, numbers that indicate quantities of something and numbers that are a part of a large set of data. It will check that you have the skills to understand all of these types of numbers, take accurate measurements, round numbers appropriately and select appropriate ways of getting the results you need.

Here is a list of exactly what you need to show you can do:

See also: **Large and small numbers**, page 11.

- **Plan a substantial and complex activity.** You will need to show that you have broken it down into a series of tasks.

- **Use information from different sources, including a large data set.** A large data set includes over 50 items and you must use this to meet the purpose of your activity.

- **Work with estimation to help you plan.** Multiplying and dividing numbers of any size rounded to 1 significant figure.

- **Take accurate and reliable observations over time.** You must use suitable equipment to measure in a variety of appropriate units.

- **Work with scale drawings, graphs, complex tables and charts.**

- **Work with ways of writing very large and very small numbers.** (For instance £1.5 billion or 2.4×10^{-3}). You will need to show you can handle formats like 2.4×10^3 or 2.4×10^{-3} or combine words and numbers like £1.8 billion or £24K (K is a way of saying 1000, so £24K = £24 000). It can be any way of writing large and small numbers, so focus on examples that might be used in qualifications or activities you are doing.

- **Understand and use compound measures.** For example speed in kilometres per hour (kph), pressure in pounds per square inch (psi) and concentrations in parts per million (ppm). Concentrate on the types of compound measures you may come across in your other courses or activities. Each area will have measures more relevant to it and used more frequently than other measures. You might find it useful to take some time to identify what these types of compound measures are in the areas you are studying.

- **Select appropriate methods for obtaining the results you need and justify your choice.** Here you are being asked to show that you can make judgements and decide how best to get the results you need. This ties in with the planning part of this section. It is asking you to show you are confident enough to know how to get the information you need.

Some compound measures may also provide evidence for working with very small numbers (e.g. ppm). Make your calculations work harder for you as evidence by having them show that you can do a range of things.

Collecting evidence

All examples are suggestions that you could try as a way of practising. There is not enough space to put in proper explanations of the methods suggested or justify what is suggested. You will have to do this when you generate your evidence for real.

The Bottom Line

HOW TO GET YOUR EVIDENCE

What you need to do	Scale drawing	Gambling habits
What is your purpose and how are you going to get the information you need in order to meet your purpose?	I want to create a scale drawing of a table.	I want to investigate people's gambling habits by looking at spending on the national lottery.
Get the information you need. You must show you can use different sources of information.	This means choosing appropriate measuring equipment, taking accurate measurements, looking at other scale drawings to help choose an appropriate scale.	I will do some research to find national data but I will also carry out a local investigation. I will look at the amounts and types of spending during one hour in my local shop.
You will need to show you can use at least two different sources in total. One of your sources of information you use at some point must include a large set of data (over 50 items).		I could observe and record using the tally method or I could simply record the spending as a list and rework the data later.
Use appropriate methods to get the results you need from the information you have collected and explain why they are appropriate.		All information will be typed into a spreadsheet.
		I will choose an hour on Saturday evening, when I know it will be busy.

Continued on page 46

Evidence requirements in a nutshell

You need to have a purpose for gathering the number information and a plan of how you are going to get hold of it. Having done this, you need to get the information and work out how you are going to get the results you need using appropriate methods. You must have evidence to show you can use at least two different sources of number information, and one of these sources must involve a data set of more than 50 items.

Hints for interpreting information at level 3

- Keep a written record of your purpose and your planning.
- Keep a written record of how or where you found the sources of information.
- Keep copies of source materials.
- Keep a copy of the graph that you have used and the information you got from it.
- Always have written evidence explaining why you chose to do what you did.

Carrying out calculations

What you must learn to do

You will probably have to carry out several different calculations in order to meet this part of the evidence requirements. Some will be part of larger activities, others might be smaller, individual calculations. Make sure you keep clear records, so you know what you have done and other people can follow it too.

Try to focus on all the calculations that can be done during the course of your other studies or activities, rather than doing calculations for their own sake. By applying relevant calculations to your other work you will find the number work more meaningful and more useful. You will also build up your portfolio in number and help your other studies too.

Take time to plan what number work can be applied to your other studies or activities. Then you can deal with how you can generate evidence for other calculations. Here is exactly what you need to show you can do:

- **Present your methods clearly and work to appropriate levels of accuracy.** These calculations can be anything from calculating areas for rooms of unusual shape, finding the volume of a sphere, converting from Celsius to Fahrenheit, working out compound interest on your savings account or even how much water there is in your local swimming pool. Try to work with the calculations that are relevant to you.

- **Perform multi-step calculations with numbers of any size.**

- **Work with powers and roots.**

- **Calculate missing angles and sides in right-angled triangles.** You have to work out the unknown angles and lengths from known sides and angles. This is checking to see if you know your triangles (page 36).

- **Calculate proportional change.**

- **Calculate actual measurements from scale drawings and scale quantities up and down.** This could be an Ordnance Survey map, a site plan, an architectural drawing or even a plan for building a scale model.

- **Work with large data sets (over 50 items).** This involves using measures of average and range to compare distributions, and estimating mean, median and range of grouped data.

- **Rearrange and use formulas, equations and expressions.** For example, if you know a circle's circumference is 18.84 cm and you need to find out the radius r (perhaps because you want to go on to find out the area of the circle) then you might do the following calculation:

$2\pi r = 18.84$	the circumference
$2 \times 3.14 \times r = 18.84$	substitute π to 2 dp
$6.28 \times r = 18.84$	multiply by 2
$r = 18.84/6.28$	rearrange to find r
$r = 3$	the answer

- **Check to identify any errors in your methods and your results.**

> Sometimes your formula work will also show that you can do multi-step calculations, and even work with powers or roots.

Collecting evidence

HOW TO GET YOUR EVIDENCE

What you need to do	Temperature conversion	Gambling habits Continued from page 43
Show you can do calculations using amounts and sizes, scales and proportions; show you can work with statistics, use formulas, and rearrange formulas.	Having found out the temperature in degrees Celsius, I want to convert it to Fahrenheit. I will use the formula to make the conversion.	Having collected my large data set of lottery buying information, I can work out the range of spending and calculate the relevant averages.
Make sure you have a clear record of all the working out you did (your methods) for each of your calculations.	To check my answer, I will rearrange the formula to give me the Fahrenheit to Celsius conversion, then substitute in my Fahrenheit answer to see if I get the original Celsius reading.	I can use total spending to make estimates and predictions, taking time to explain their reliability (perhaps the data was collected during busy time).
Work to an appropriate level of accuracy in your calculations, keeping a note of what it is and why it is appropriate.		I can work out the relationship of £1 players to the rest, expressing this as a percentage, ratio and fraction.
Then make sure that your answers are correct by checking your calculations and correcting any mistakes.		*Continued on page 48*

You need to show that you can work with a large set of data in your calculating work, at least once.

Evidence requirements in a nutshell

You need to have evidence in your portfolio showing that you can do four different types of calculation. You must show you can do calculations that are to do with:

- Amounts and sizes
- Scales and proportions
- Handling statistics
- Rearranging and using formulas

Make sure that each time you do any of these calculations you have clear records of how you got the answers (your methods). Include in these records how you checked your answers and how you corrected any mistakes that you found. Make sure the results of the calculations make sense and that you have worked to an appropriate level of accuracy. Some calculations have got to involve using a large data set.

Hints for carrying out calculations at level 3

- Have four separate records that show your calculations for (a) amounts and sizes, (b) scales and proportion, (c) handling with statistics, (d) rearranging and using formulas.
- Maybe use them as subsections in the Calculations section of your number portfolio.
- Show your way of working out each calculation (your methods). It is important to keep this as a record, even if you go back over your work and find mistakes, you should keep a record of this. This is proof that you checked your own work and were able to correct it.
- Keep notes or other records showing how you worked out what would be an appropriate level of accuracy and why you thought it was an appropriate level.

Interpreting results and presenting your findings

What you must learn to do

Whether you have gathered information, carried out calculations or just have some results to present, you need to show you can choose appropriate ways to present your findings and explain why you think they are appropriate. Having chosen your methods of presenting, you need to show you can use them correctly and present your work in a clear and correct manner. You also need to show you can draw conclusions based on your work.

In other words, you must show you can:

- **Use appropriate methods to illustrate findings, show trends and make comparisons.**

- **Construct and label charts, graphs, diagrams and scale drawings using accepted conventions.** Whether you are producing pie charts, frequency tables, graphs or workshop drawings, you must show that you can correctly label your work. This is to help others read and understand your work. Remember that very often the point of using methods like graphs or diagrams is to help others understand your work more easily. Correct labelling helps.

- **Make appropriate conclusions based on your findings.** You should always include details of how possible sources of error might have affected your results.

- **Examine critically, and justify, your choice of methods and explain how your results relate to the purpose of your activity.** Remember that the whole exercise is about showing you can read, interpret, calculate and present numbers to meet your purposes or needs. So it is important to explain how your number work helped you meet your needs.

This will help others understand the reasons you had for making the decisions you made. This applies to the equipment you used, the accuracy you worked to, the calculations you made, or anything else you did. It also gives you an opportunity to show that they were the appropriate choices and to explain why, given your circumstances and purpose.

Collecting evidence

HOW TO GET YOUR EVIDENCE		
What you need to do	*Share prices*	*Gambling habits* *Continued from page 46*
Look at the results from calculations you have made and identify good ways of presenting this information.	I have recorded the performance of a share price of a company over one month looking at the share prices in the financial	Having got all this lottery information and performed calculations on the data, I now need to present my findings.

EVIDENCE OF LEVEL 3 | **49**

Present the information clearly.

Explain why you think the ways you have chosen to present your results are effective and the most appropriate.

When you are producing evidence for this section, make sure you will have at least one graph, one chart and one diagram in your portfolio.

Describe how your results help you meet the purpose of your task.

section of a newspaper (e.g. the *Guardian*).

I have calculated the range of movement from lowest to highest price, and compared it to the index of top shares (FTSE index).

I now want the changes to be very clear, so I need to pick an appropriate scale for the y-axis. The x-axis is used to mark the different days.

Having worked out the lowest share price as £3.17, I don't need to start the y-axis at 0 but could start it at £3. This will help me use a larger scale on the y-axis to accentuate the daily differences and fluctuations in price.

(See page 144 for further examples.)

I can present the spending patterns by using a bar chart, grouping the different levels of spending appropriately. For example, I could put the numbers of people on the y-axis and put the amounts on the x-axis (£1, £2, £3, etc. or £1, £2–5, £6–10, etc.)The choice of scale, depends on my data and my purpose.

I can also present the information on a pie chart or stack graph, either showing all categories or just the £1 spenders.

Evidence requirements in a nutshell

You need to show that you can select good ways to present number information you have collected or generated. It is important to keep records explaining the reasons for the choices you are making when you select different ways to present information. This helps the person marking your work to understand your thinking.

Somewhere in this part of your portfolio you will have to show you can present information using a graph, a chart and a diagram that you have created. You will also need to include in your work a note explaining how the results of your calculations meet your purpose.

Hints for interpreting results and presenting your findings at level 3

- Make sure each of your charts and diagrams has clear labels and a title that explains what it shows.
- Make sure you have used the correct units of measurement for what you have measured.
- Check that you have used appropriate scales and axes.
- Remembering to give evidence that you can present your information using at least one graph, one chart and one diagram

Other forms of assessment and evidence

External assessment at level 3

You will need to take an external assessment as well as produce a portfolio of number evidence. The external assessment is designed to show that you can work with numbers at the correct level under a different set of circumstances. Normally, for your portfolio work, you will try to use the other courses that you are doing as a way of helping generate your number evidence. This time, in the external assessment, you will not know what the questions are.

What will the external assessment ask questions about?

The external assessment can only ask you questions on the number key skill. Therefore, everything that is asked has to be based on what is in the key skill specification. You cannot be asked something that is not based on the key skill specification at the level you are taking. The people who write the tests know this and have been told to make sure they stick to the number work in the key skill.

All this means that you really know what type of questions will be asked in the test. You may not know exactly what the questions will be about, but you will know what level they will be set at and you will know the type of number work that will be involved.

External assessments will be set by your key skills awarding body and may involve a series of tasks about numbers that you must do within a certain time period. Even if you are allowed to use a calculator, remember that it will also be important to write down all your working clearly.

What is the point of an external assessment?

The idea of an external assessment is to provide an opportunity for you to show that you can carry out different number work to complete tasks set by other people.

It also shows that you can do larger, related tasks under controlled conditions (a time limit and with someone else setting the tasks). Here is how to look at it:

- The portfolio shows that you can set your own number tasks, you can carry them out with and without a calculator, and you can meet your own deadlines and time constraints.
- The external assessments show that you can do number in a restricted amount of time. You will know what the questions are likely to involve but you will not know exactly what they are about. It also shows that you can carry out number tasks set by other people.

When you meet these requirements, you will get your key skill in Application of Number, and you will have proved that you can do the number work under a range of different conditions and in different contexts.

Part 3: Opportunities

This part highlights opportunities for generating number evidence in the qualifications you are taking. It will show you:

- How your qualifications can be used to generate number evidence.
- Where the best opportunities for this evidence arise in the qualifications.

This part is divided into three sections:

- **Evidence from A-level courses:** You will find this section useful whichever awarding body you are with.
- **Evidence from Vocational A-level courses:** This section will be useful regardless of whether you are working towards a 6-unit or 12-unit award.
- **Evidence from everyday sources:** This section will show you how you already use numbers as part of your everyday life.

The examples provided should be seen as starting points for generating evidence. You will see that some qualifications provide more opportunities than others. However, all contain some opportunities and will at least get you started. Make sure that you take time to read not just your subjects but also subjects that are related to the ones you are taking. This will help you gain a fuller understanding of how and where number evidence can be produced. For example, if you are doing a Business Vocational A-level then also look at the Business A-level and the Retail and Distributive Services Vocational A-level. You may also want to check out the Leisure and Tourism Vocational A-levels.

Vocational awards

The GNVQ Advanced awards are now called Vocational A-levels. From September 2001 GNVQ Foundation and Intermediate awards are likely to be known as Vocational GCSEs.

Evidence from A-level courses

Art A-level

About the syllabus

The Art awards aim to combine intellectual and creative development with analytical, experimental and technical skills. They are also intended to help you develop aesthetic understanding and critical judgement. The programmes of learning associated with these awards are intended to provide you with an appreciation of the interconnectedness of art, craft and design and their roles in different societies and cultures, both contemporary and historical.

See also: **Art and Design Vocational A-level**, page 84

Topic area 1
Sculpture or 3D studies

Planning and interpreting information

The production of a 3D outcome is a substantial and complex activity that will need to be broken down into a series of tasks. As you prepare to work in three dimensions you will need to undertake planning and preparation including the necessary exploration and research, deciding on the media and materials you will use and the technology and equipment you will need to access.

Objects and artefacts are usually produced as the result of exploration and research that look at a range of different sources to meet the purpose of your project. You will need to decide upon the formal elements you wish to use and estimate the amount of time and range of media and materials you will need.

Art, craft and design outcomes will usually be the result of accurate and carefully constructed drawings produced as a result of personal observations. The extent to which these developments are recorded and retained will determine the contribution they can make to your Application of Number portfolio.

Calculating

The achievement of 3D outcomes in art, craft and design from drawings and plans will require you to calculate or work out how to scale up from plans or models and maquettes. The extent to which your finished work matches your original intentions will in part be decided by how accurately you can use ratios to scale up and retain original proportions. Your numerical skills will also be required in the costing and selection of media and materials either for you to buy or as part of a response to a potential client or sponsor.

You will not normally think of art, craft and design as providing or requiring you to calculate but when dealing with a project, responding to a brief or producing an object or artefact from drawings you will need to back up your creativity with some accurate calculations and hard data.

Interpreting results and presenting findings

The finished object or artefact or the presentational portfolio should be seen as the result of your calculations. An exhibition, presentation or discussion of this is an example of how you present your findings. Schematic drawings or plans should be seen as diagrams in this context. You should be able to explain clearly and effectively how you have costed or scaled up during the creative process.

Topic area 2
Personal studies and investigations

Personal studies and investigations give you the opportunity to do what you want with the media and materials you want to work with.

As with any extended project, you will have to plan carefully and this can best be done by breaking down your project into a series of tasks. They could be investigation of sources and collection of information; experimentation and exploration of ideas, media and materials; and then presenting a personal outcome based on your appreciation of what you found out or did.

The amount of number you use during your study or investigation will depend upon your chosen project. The opportunities you will have will also vary according to individual areas you have chosen to study. Graphics, textiles and photography are rich in opportunities to interpret information from scale drawings, tables and charts as you prepare and plan.

These areas of study also provide ample opportunity for multi-stage calculations to do with amounts and sizes, scales and proportions as sketches and studies are enlarged and prepared for illustrations or swatches and as negatives are developed then enlarged and printed into photographs.

All aspects of art, craft and design provide opportunities for you to present your interpretations and discuss them with others. The extent to which they can satisfy the Application of Number requirements for interpreting results and presenting findings will depend upon how you have used numeracy, how much you have understood the contribution that numeracy has made and the effectiveness of your explanations and presentations, either orally or through annotations and other records.

Further opportunities for evidence

The following areas of individual study may also prove valuable in generating Application of Number evidence:

- there are several specialist areas of study offered and recognised by most Art A-level specifications and these offer particularly relevant opportunities to provide number evidence:
  - **Fine art**: calculations to do with amounts and sizes, especially when mixing media or deciding on materials required.
  - **3D studies**: calculations to do with scales and proportions when working with batch sizes and timing in ceramics; similar calculations for detailed scale drawings required by theatre, product and environmental design.
- **Graphics**: calculations using scales and proportions for page layouts and print runs.
- **Textiles**: calculations to do with amounts and sizes in relation to surface decoration, and dyeing.
- **Photography**: use of formulas during developing and printing.

Remember that this is not a definitive list and other aspects of art will require you to use number effectively and with a degree of precision that is particular to specialist methods or processes.

Biology A-level

About the syllabus

The Biology award aims to develop essential knowledge and understanding in biology and how to use them in new and changing situations. It will also help you develop an understanding of scientific methods and the contribution of new technology, particularly information and communication technology. The programmes of learning will also help you to recognise the role and responsible use of biology in society and sustain and develop your enjoyment and interest in biology.

Topic area 1
Working on your experimental skills

Planning and interpreting information

You will develop planning skills that will require you to identify and define the nature of the task or problem and combine available information with your own knowledge and understanding. You will need to select equipment, procedures, methods and materials then decide on appropriate measurements to use and observations to make which will generate useful and reliable results.

In executing your experiments you will be expected to use apparatus correctly and safely and work in a methodical and organised way, taking

What you must know
Part 1: The Learning Curve will help you with the knowledge you need.

What you must do
Part 2: The Bottom Line will help you with the evidence you need

See also: **Science Vocational A-level**, page 119

due care for the well-being of living organisms and the environment. You must make and record observations and make measurements to the required degree of accuracy and precision.

The measuring skills that you use in your experimental work will require you to make accurate and reliable observations over time and, where necessary, understand and use compound measures.

All of these skills are central to the Application of Number key skill and your work in biology. Make sure that you carefully and reliably record your findings, the methods you choose and the reasons for your selection.

Calculating

Experimental work will produce information and data that will need to be ordered and manipulated using calculations and other mathematical processes. Your biology course will teach you how to use a range of arithmetical and graphical techniques and how to check your methods and results. See the notes at the end of this section.

Depending on the experiments done and the measurements taken, you will normally have the opportunity to work with a large data set (no less that 50 items) where you will use the measures of average and range to compare distributions and estimate mean, median and range of grouped data. Always make sure you use checking procedures to identify potential errors in methods and results.

See also: **Land and Environment**, page 105

Interpreting results and presenting findings

Communication of your findings in terms of biological information and ideas will require you to select and use appropriate methods to illustrate findings, show trends and make comparisons.

You will be expected to use tables, charts, diagrams and graphs to present and justify your analysis. In presenting your findings you will need to recognise and comment on the trends and patterns in the data.

Your presentation will include an explanation of how your experiments, the data they have produced and the calculations you have undertaken, have resulted in valid conclusions that relate to the original purpose of the task or problem.

This evidence, together with developmental records and evaluation of evidence and procedures that comprise the investigation, will provide evidence of your ability to plan and carry out a substantial and complex activity for level 3 of the Application of Number key skill.

Topic area 2
Preparing for your practical examinations

Practical examinations will build on your experience, knowledge and techniques developed during your work on experimental skills. The examinations will try to determine how well you can carry out the process on your own. In preparing and practising for this task you will have the opportunity to develop a range of skills that will generate authentic evidence for your Application of Number key skill.

Opportunities

As you found in your investigation work, the basic framework for experimenting equates to the Application of Number structure. Here are the abilities you will be developing. The practical skills are shown in bold and the Application of Number sections are shown in brackets:

- **Plan and implement** (planning an activity and interpreting information)
  - A testable hypothesis is planned.
  - Apparatus and procedures are stated and the number and type of measurements are appropriate and relevant.
  - Measurements and observations are accurate and reliable.
- **Analyse evidence** (carry out calculations)
  - Observations and calculations are presented; graphs are drawn.
  - Trends and patterns in data are identified.
- **Analyse and evaluate evidence** (interpreting results and presenting findings)
  - Charts, diagrams, graphs and tables are used to present findings.
  - Trends and patterns are explained; inconsistencies are identified and commented on.
  - Inconsistencies are used to explain limitations of experimental techniques.
  - Explanations of how the chosen methods relate to the original purpose.

The extent to which this exercise and the of the Application of Number requirements match will depend upon how well you record your planning and your calculations and how well you present them.

Further opportunities for evidence

The Biology A-level has specific requirements for mathematics. When developing, practising or using these techniques during your course you will have the opportunity to produce evidence for the calculation section of the key skills unit.

- **Arithmetic and computations:** you will be expected to use decimals and standard form, as well as ratios, fractions and percentages; you will also be expected to make estimates. These will contribute to the key skill evidence for amounts and sizes, scales and proportion.
- **Handling data:** you will be expected to work with significant figures and arithmetic means; you will be expected to construct and interpret frequency tables and diagrams, bar charts and histograms. These will contribute to the key skills evidence for handling statistics.
- **Algebra:** you will be expected to change the subject of an equation and substitute algebraic equations for numerical values. This will enable you to present evidence for rearranging and using formulas.
- **Graphs:** you will be expected to translate information between graphical, numerical and algebraic forms, plot two variables from experimental or other data, and calculate a rate of change from a

What you must know
Part 1: The Learning Curve will help you with the knowledge you need.

What you must do
Part 2: The Bottom Line will help you with the evidence you need

linear graph. These will contribute to the key skills evidence for handling statistics and support the presentation of your results.

Business Studies A-level

About the syllabus

The Business Studies award aims to develop an understanding of organisations, the markets they serve and the process of adding value. It will help you to understand business behaviour from the customer, manager, creditor, owner and employee perspectives and improve your own decision-making and problem-solving skills.

Topic area 1
Marketing

See also: **Business Vocational A-level**, page 88

Planning and interpreting information

You will need to understand how a business behaves as it looks to find then satisfy its customers. This will require you to develop Planning skills, which will involve setting objectives, deciding where to seek information, the methods you can use to collect information and how to interpret the information you collect.

You must make sure that your methods and sources provide you with accurate, reliable and relevant data and information. Your market research techniques should include a large data set; along with records of your planning including aims, objectives and strategy, this will generate evidence for the planning and interpreting information component of your Application of Number portfolio.

Calculating

In carrying out your market research you will have collected a range of statistics which should provide you with information and data to determine changing customer needs and inform your sales forecasting and pricing strategies.

Your work on marketing will require you to analyse your findings to identify factors which may influence demand for products and services and this is likely to require multi-step calculation.

Depending on the focus of your market and marketing researches, you will generate evidence for the carrying out calculations component of your Application of Number portfolio. You should certainly have the opportunity to calculate using amounts and sizes and demonstrate your ability to handle statistics.

Interpreting results and presenting findings

The results of the calculations you have made will be used to inform your understanding of market behaviour including current share and anticipated growth. The extent to which your work in this aspect of Business Studies meets the Application of Number requirements will depend upon

how you present your findings, using graphs, charts and diagrams. It will also depend upon how you justify your methods by explaining how your calculations relate to the original objectives for your marketing strategy.

Topic area 2
Accounting and finance

Planning and interpreting information

You will need to demonstrate how accounting and financial information are used to assist decision making and financial control in business organisations.

You will need to understand the purpose of budgets, the role of balance sheets and profit and loss accounts and how to clarify and analyse different types of costs.

In developing the knowledge, skills and understanding listed here you will need to work with relevant sources of information and data from a range of organisations. This will require you to read and understand the balance sheets of different organisations and demonstrate an understanding of very large numbers.

When planning and undertaking your activities, make sure that your observations are accurate and reliable and that you always use the appropriate units.

Calculating

Although you are not required to construct accounts of your own you will be expected to modify the accounts of others and use ratios to assess profitability and liquidity.

Your course will teach you how to read and analyse balance sheets and how to use arithmetical and graphical techniques as well as specific formulas in order to calculate gross and net profit and demonstrate the relationship between costs and levels of output.

Always calculate to the appropriate level of accuracy, show your working methods, and check your results to ensure errors are found and corrected, particularly when working with very large numbers.

Interpreting results and presenting findings

The central purpose of accounting and finance is to ensure that business decisions are made in the light of the strategic objectives of the business and shaped by financial information and data.

Your planning and calculations should show that you understand how budgets are used for income and expenditure, the differences between cash flow and profit and how to interpret a balance sheet and a profit and loss account.

Your results should combine both qualitative and quantitative factors that will inform forecasting and investment as you evaluate and present the business position of your chosen activity.

The extent to which you will generate valid evidence for the Application of Number key skill will depend upon your selection of appropri-

What you must know
Part 1: The Learning Curve will help you with the knowledge you need.

What you must do
Part 2: The Bottom Line will help you with the evidence you need

ate methods and your use of graphs, charts and diagrams to explain how your results relate to the original purpose of your activity.

Chemistry A-level

About the syllabus

The Chemistry award aims to develop essential knowledge and understanding in chemistry and how to use them in new and changing situations. It will also help you develop an understanding of the connection between theory and experiment and how advances in information technology and instrumentation are used in chemistry. The programmes of learning will also help you to appreciate the role and responsible use of scientific knowledge and evidence in society as well as sustain and develop your enjoyment and interest in chemistry.

Topic area 1
Applying your knowledge and understanding

Planning and interpreting information

You will be expected to develop planning skills which will require you to draw on existing relevant information, then select, organise and present this information clearly and logically. You will be expected to select equipment, procedures, methods and materials and decide upon how to describe, explain and interpret phenomena and effects in terms of chemical principles and concepts.

A recognised source of information is the periodic table with respect to elements and their compounds. This, and other tables, diagrams and graphs, will provide an opportunity for you to demonstrate your understanding and interpretative skills as you translate information from one form into another and present data in an appropriate format.

All of the skills identified here will contribute to your chemistry and your Application of Number key skill. Make sure that you carefully and reliably record your findings, the methods you choose and the reasons for your selection.

Calculating

Opportunities will naturally arise throughout the course where you will need to order or manipulate information and data using both arithmetical and mathematical techniques and calculations. Your chemistry courses require you to know and use a range of arithmetical and graphical techniques and how to check your methods and results. See the notes at the end of this section.

The data and information you work with will depend upon the experiments done and the measurements taken. However, scales and proportion are important skills to the chemist. They link to amounts and sizes because proportionality will help you work out the quantities needed to carry out a reaction on different scales. Formulas are also central to many of your

See also: **Science Vocational A-level**, page 119.

Opportunities

calculations and rearranging them properly should be practised and recorded. Always make sure that you use checking procedures to identify potential errors in methods and results.

Interpreting results and presenting findings

Assessing the validity of your chemical information, experiments and calculations are fundamental skills. You will be expected to interpret your results, present your findings and justify your methods. Both practical and theory exercises will provide you with opportunities to present results graphically using graphs, charts and diagrams. The analysis of chemical data and identification of trends and patterns should help you to explain and justify the activity.

Topic area 2
Working on your experimental and investigational skills

Planning and interpreting information

You will be required to develop and plan an experimental and investigational activity. This is best done by breaking it down into a series of tasks that use appropriate skills and techniques. You will need to demonstrate safe and skilful working practices and make accurate and reliable observations using suitable equipment, measuring quantitites in the appropriate units and with the appropriate precision. You will be expected to choose appropriate methods for obtaining and recording the results you need.

Calculating

Experimental work will require you to process your qualitative data using a variety of techniques. You will be expected to know how to translate units from one form into another, how to organise data into diagrams, graphs and tables and to use and rearrange formulas according to the experiments carried out and the data collected.

Although a large data set is not a central requirement of the chemistry specification, opportunities may be created during your course work to work with one or more sets of data. Errors can occur during calculations and you will be expected to show how you have used checking procedures to identify and correct errors in methods and results.

Interpreting results and presenting findings

You will be expected to interpret, explain, evaluate and communicate the results of your experimental and investigative work clearly and logically. This is a central requirement of the Application of Number key skill on interpreting results and presenting your findings. You will have learned how to present your results graphically as this is a natural part of the chemistry course. Your presentation should include an explanation, using appropriate specialist vocabulary, of how your experiments, the resulting data and any calculations relate to the original task or problem.

This evidence, together with your developmental and planning records, should provide evidence of your ability to plan and carry out the substantial and complex activity required by the level 3 Application of Number key skill.

Further opportunities for evidence

The Chemistry A level has specific requirements for mathematics. When developing, practising or using these techniques during your course, you will have the opportunity to produce evidence for the calculation section of the key skill unit.

- **Arithmetic and computation:** you will be expected to use decimals, standard form, ratios, fractions and percentages and make estimates of your calculations. These will contribute evidence for amounts and sizes, scales and proportion
- **Handling data:** you will be expected to work with significant figures and arithmetic means; you will also be expected to interpret frequency tables and diagrams, bar charts and histograms. These will contribute to key skills evidence for handling statistics.
- **Algebra:** you will be expected to change the subject of an equation, substitute algebraic equations for numerical values and use logarithms. These skills will enable you to present evidence for rearranging and using formulas.
- **Geometry:** you will be expected to appreciate angles and shapes in 2D and 3D structures and represent them two-dimensionally. This will enable you to present evidence for calculations to do with scales and proportion and support your interpretation and presentation key skill.
- **Graphs:** you will be expected to translate information between graphical, numerical and algebraic forms, plot two variables from experimental or other data, create linear graphs using $y = mx + c$ and determine the gradient and intercept of linear graphs and, where necessary, use the tangent to a curve to measure the rate of change. These skills will contribute to key skills evidence for scales and proportion and handling statistics. Depending on how and where graphs are used, you may have evidence for your interpretation and presentation key skill.

What you must know
Part 1: The Learning Curve will help you with the knowledge you need.

What you must do
Part 2: The Bottom Line will help you with the evidence you need

Opportunities

Computing A-level

About the syllabus

There is a clear relationship between the content of the Computing A-level and that of the Information and Communication Technology (ICT) Vocational A-level so the following text is relevant to both awards.

Your course may include the study and the application of different methods of representing numbers. In addition to the denary system (base 10) it may include binary (base 2), hexdecimal (base 16) representation of integers, floating point numbers, and binary coded decimal (BCD). There will also be opportunities to work with data communication, the Internet and a range of different hardware and software.

You should also look at working on course work or projects as a major opportunity to generate number evidence. This is partly because you are in charge of some of the direction your work takes, so you can lean towards numbers more heavily if you wish. This may have the added benefit of improving the quality of your computing work and the depth of your understanding about the area.

About the Vocational A-level award

The ICT Vocational A-level award will often have a different emphasis on how you use the knowledge, skills and understanding that you gain in doing the course. It will also adopt a more applied approach, emphasising the vocational interpretation of the content and trying to help you understand how IT is used in the working world.

Remember to look at optional units as a chance to continue generating number evidence and keep in mind that some optional units will be better than others for creating number opportunities. If you have some influence over the optional units you can take, you should keep this in mind as one factor to help you choose.

Topic area 1
Don't overlook the obvious

When you use (or especially when you buy) a computer you are constantly bombarded with different ways of talking about, using and presenting numbers. You may need to compare the capacity and speed of access of various media like magnetic tape and disk, optical media and CD-ROM. This is a basic numbers comparison and should provide you with lots of opportunity to generate evidence.

When your course looks at principles of electronic data communication and modems, there will be opportunities using a whole series of numbers relating to average connection speeds (bps), average download speed (Kbps). These are both compound measures used to express numbers (see the planning and interpreting requirements in the key skill).

Your course may start with a look at BIOS systems, and the initial BIOS screen on your PC will show the basic numbers important to the machine. Here you can look for opportunities to generate number evidence and make sure you understand the basic numbers important to the machines you use.

The following information was taken from an American computing magazine and was used to describe a notebook (laptop) computer:

- 750 MHz AMD K6 CPU
- 64 MB SDRAM (192 MB max)
- 1 MB L2 cache, 8 MB VRAM
- 14.1 active matrix XTG display
- 16 GB UDMA hard drive, 1.44 MB floppy
- 12.2 × 10.1 × 1.97 inches, 7.95 pounds
  (the USA still uses imperial measurements)
- one-year warranty ($2345 rrp).

This list includes all sizes and types of numbers. When you come to look at hardware, or better still make comparisons, you will get all sorts of opportunities to interpret, calculate and present using these numbers. You work with approximation the entire time. Look at the following information on real memory quantities.

Term	Abbreviation	Approximation	Real size
Byte		1	1
Kilobyte	K or KB	1 000	1 024
Megabyte	M or MB	1 000 000	1 048 576
Gigabyte	G or GB	1 000 000 000	1 073 741 824
Terabyte	T or TB	1 000 000 000 000	1 099 511 627 776

Topic area 2
Working with number bases

Planning and interpreting information
Here are some of the opportunities:

- Explaining the use of different number bases and other number representations requires you to make decisions about what stages are involved, how you will clearly show the processes, and what presentation techniques you can use.
- The interpretation of complex tables required by the key skills specification occurs naturally when translating between number bases. You may also be reading other forms of graphics.
- You will also be producing evidence needed for the key skill as you explain and demonstrate how computers handle very large and very small numbers.
- Representation of negative integers by two's complement and sign and magnitude method and describing the conventions for storing negative values and the use of two's complement to perform subtraction.

In particular, look for opportunities when you:

- Explain the conversion of denary to binary and use hex as shorthand for binary.
- Work on representation of integers and fixed point numbers.
- Work with binary coded decimal and explain BCD format and its advantages.
- Compare the precision and range of various number systems, according to their representation.

Calculating

The key skill requirement to show methods clearly and work to appropriate levels of accuracy coincides with your course requirement for clarity and accuracy in describing and working with number systems. The nature of the topic requires you to consider the precision of various number systems and their representation.

You will probably use practical examples to explain the representation of numbers and translation between different forms. You should consider examples that include the following types of evidence:

- Multi-step calculations
- Use of powers and roots
- Working with large data sets
- Working with formulas

There may also be opportunities to gather evidence if you work on:

- Rounding errors and truncation errors
- Floating point numbers
- Floating point numbers lead to the concept of mantissa and exponent, the need for normalisation and how normalising affects the range and precision of the number represented.

Interpreting results and presenting findings

To explain the different ways in which numbers are represented and handled by computer systems, you will need to accurately interpret the system and select appropriate methods of presenting the information. Graphic forms such as comparison tables could be used to help you in your explanations.

Your course may require you to discuss and consider the merits of various number systems and their representation. If so, this will help generate evidence for the key skill which asks you to show you can make critical judgements about numbers.

Topic area 3
Working with spreadsheets

You may find that in working with spreadsheets you are able to pick up number evidence to show that you can handle statistics, deal with complex data and carry out calculations using formulas. This really depends on the nature of your work and the focus of your activity. However, you may find there is an opportunity to generate evidence for numbers if you check your computer work, if you double-check results by annotating your printouts, or even if you are in the development and design stages and are carrying out some preparatory work.

Spreadsheet work will provide several different opportunities to show you can present data effectively and appropriately. This will also allow you to examine critically and justify your methods and the selections you made. Your spreadsheet work could be used to show you can construct and label charts, graphs and diagrams correctly and that you are able to use them to draw appropriate conclusions. Look for opportunities to present results in the following graphical forms:

- Line graphs
- Bar charts
- Pie charts
- Use of picture markers
- Scatter charts

Show that you can present charts and line graphs appropriately, including the use of:

- Chart or graph title
- Axis labels
- Background
- Legend data series label
- Data labels
- Category labels
- Axis formats
- Axis values
- Gridlines

What you must know
Part 1: The Learning Curve will help you with the knowledge you need.

What you must do
Part 2: The Bottom Line will help you with the evidence you need

Design and Technology A-level

About the syllabus
The Design and Technology award aims to develop innovation, creativity, design capability, recognition of constraints and the ability to produce high quality products. It will provide the opportunity for you to select and apply knowledge, understanding and the skills of the design production processes to a range of technological activities.

The programmes of study will provide you with the opportunity to develop a critical understanding of design and technology activities from contemporary and historical practices. You will be expected to be able to use a full range of knowledge, skills, understanding, attitudes and aptitudes inherent in design and technological activity and make informed choices on appropriate applications and uses. These skills are at the centre of key skills capability and confidence.

The assignment will be based on a range of planning activities. These

activities are identical for both the design dimension of A-level and the planning aspect of the Application of Number unit.

See also: **Engineering Vocational A-level**, page 97

Topic area 1
Product development (designing)

Planning and interpreting information

The area of specialism you have chosen – product design, food, systems and control – will require you to undertake a design and make assignment. You will need to identify, explore and analyse a range of user needs and problems to generate sufficient information to inform the development of your design brief.

The information can come from primary sources such as other people's data or information published by manufacturers or consumer organisations. This research is likely to result in you making accurate and reliable observations, reading charts and tables and reading and understanding complex numerical and statistical data.

Once you have collected sufficient data you will be expected to assemble, organise and use this information to choose appropriate methods for undertaking the product design.

Calculating

You will be expected to generate and develop a range of design ideas. You will be required to interpret and use the information collected and then use design and technology techniques to develop and refine your ideas into designs.

Your designs will use different types of calculations and representations depending on the context and focus of your award. However, it is likely that design will require you to work with amounts and sizes, scales and proportion as you use graphical and numerical expressions to develop scale drawings and scale quantities up and down.

An essential aspect of the key skill and the design and technology programme is ensuring that your methods are clear and accurate and your results are checked to identify and correct any errors. Ensure throughout that you have logically and competently recorded actions, decisions and calculations.

Interpreting results and presenting findings

The strategies for developing, representing, evaluating and presenting your idea will need to be carefully chosen. You will be expected to illustrate these ideas using established design and technology conventions and methods including modelling, charts, diagrams along with appropriate tables and graphs. The critical aspects of your presentation will be the extent to which your designs meet the original purpose or design specification and the unambiguous way in which others interpret your presentation and findings.

Topic area 2
Product development (making)

See also:
**Manufacturing
Technology
Vocational A-level**,
page 111

Planning and interpreting information

You will be expected to develop, produce or refine a production plan that will break down the complex activity of production into a series of discrete tasks. The main sources of information will be the original design specification and manufacturer and any trade information relevant to the materials and equipment that will be used. A major aspect here will be the extent to which you accurately and successfully read and understand the drawings, tables and charts associated with product realisation.

You may need to revise the production plan or the equipment and material requirements following their application, trialling or testing. Always ensure that you keep clear and logical records of this decision-making process.

Calculating

Opportunities for using amounts and sizes, scales and proportion identified in topic area 1 are likely to arise again as real materials are ordered, bought and prepared in advance of the production process.

Depending on the context or focus, more commercially based calculations could be required in developing one-off, batch or high volume products. This approach could offer more opportunities for statistical analysis of costs of production in terms of economies of scale. Costs could also inform design refinements and decisions to introduce `bought-in' parts.

The practical aspect of this work will need to demonstrate how checking procedures contribute to effective outcomes and efficient uses of equipment, materials and time.

Interpreting results and presenting findings

The product itself provides tangible evidence of how you have interpreted your calculations. You will be expected to present your product and justify its appropriateness by selecting and using methods of testing appropriate to the product type. The results of these tests could be presented against the original specification using a graphical format. The care with which you summarise and record your evaluation should provide substantial evidence for the key skill.

Further opportunities for evidence

The topic areas designing and making should each provide sufficient evidence for a substantial and complex activity that includes tasks for the key skills of planning and interpreting information, carrying out calculations and interpreting and presenting your findings. However, preparatory work in advance of these major projects may provide opportunities for evidence to be drawn from a complete design and make activity.

The programme of study itself will require a high facility in numerical capability, both in terms of interpretation of data and in calculating.

What you must know
Part 1: The Learning Curve will help you with the knowledge you need.

What you must do
Part 2: The Bottom Line will help you with the evidence you need

Opportunities

Evidence for discrete tasks should be carefully recorded to provide supporting evidence for the more complex and extended activities.

General Studies A-level

About the syllabus

The General Studies award aims to develop the ability to integrate knowledge from a range of disciplines. You will be required to demonstrate how this combined knowledge provides you with greater understanding of the issues studied. You will learn how to interpret information and make informed judgements based on the evidence available. The programmes of study will provide you with the opportunity to think constructively, critically and logically and explore a range of different approaches to problem solving. You will be expected to communicate your attitudes, ideas and solutions clearly and coherently using an appropriate format and style. The skills and knowledge you develop are at the centre of key skills capability and confidence.

Topic area 1
Science, mathematics and technology

Planning and interpreting information

You will be expected to develop planning skills that will require you to select and interpret information and data using mathematical reasoning and associated knowledge, techniques and understanding. You may be given access to selected information and data or expected to research and collect your own further information. In each case you will be expected to organise and present this combined information clearly and logically.

You will be expected to draw your information from at least two sources, given or found, and at least one of these must include a data set of over 50 items. This is likely to require you to work with grouped data and understand how to construct and interpret frequency tables and cumulative frequency diagrams.

The skills identified above are central to the requirements of the general studies programme and the key skill of Application of Number. The extent to which you satisfy the key skill will depend upon the quality of your record keeping and the clarity with which you justify your working methods.

Calculating

Any data analysis will necessitate the use of multi-step calculations to do with amounts and sizes, scales and proportion, statistics or rearranging and using formulas as you explore and develop your combined data.

The data and information you work with will depend on the focus of your individual project. If the focus is purely on scientific, mathematical and technological practice and reasoning, the data sets are likely to be based on measurements. Where the focus is more on social and economic trends and constraints, you are more likely to be working with comparisons of different groupings.

Always use checking procedures to identify potential errors in your working methods and results.

Interpreting results and presenting findings

You will be expected to use tables, charts, diagrams and graphs to communicate your findings. You will need to marshall your evidence and draw conclusions which you will present in an individual report. Together with other records, the report, should demonstrate your ability to carry through the substantial and complex activity that includes evidence of tasks for the key skills of planning and interpreting information, carrying out calculations and interpreting results, and presenting your findings. All these skills are required by Application of Number at level 3.

Topic area 2
Preparing for your examinations

The General Studies award sets examinations in three overlapping areas: science, mathematics and technology; culture, morality, arts and humanities; society, politics and the economy. Each of these areas will provide opportunities for you to demonstrate your ability to show your mathematics reasoning and its application.

In preparing and practising for these examination papers, you will need to develop the ability to interpret information, carry out and check calculations, interpret your results and present your findings. These are the skills that underpin Application of Number so, by practising and preparing for your general studies examination, you should be able to generate valid evidence for the key skill.

The different Application of Number sections you will be developing here, link with the areas as follows.

Planning an activity and interpreting information

- Understanding scientific methods, principles, criteria and their application (science, mathematics and technology)
- Creativity and innovation (culture, morality, arts and humanities)
- The nature of objectivity in social sciences; explanation and evaluation in human behaviour (society, politics and the economy).

Carry out calculations

- Mathematical reasoning and its applications (science, mathematics and technology).
- Social and economic trends and constraints (society, politics and the economy).

Interpreting results and presenting findings

- Moral responsibility: the social, ethical and environmental

LONGMAN KEY SKILLS · LEVEL 3 · APPLICATION OF NUMBER

Opportunities

implications of scientific discoveries and technological developments (science, mathematics and technology)
- Aesthetic evaluations (culture, morality, arts and humanities)
- The nature of objectivity in social sciences: explanation and evaluation of human behaviour (society, politics and the economy)

The extent to which your work in general studies meets the requirements of the key skill will depend upon the way you:

- Demonstrate relevant mathematical knowledge and understanding and apply them to the range of issues you are asked to address
- Use mathematical terms and expressions to communicate clearly and accurately.
- Use mathematical skills to marshal evidence, draw conclusions and present findings.
- Demonstrate an ability to select and apply mathematical knowledge and understanding in a balanced and purposeful manner.

What you must know
Part 1: The Learning Curve will help you with the knowledge you need.

What you must do
Part 2: The Bottom Line will help you with the evidence you need

Further opportunities for evidence

The Application of Number key skill requires you to demonstrate that you possess the appropriate level of numeracy to enable you to apply the key skill effectively. Where the General Studies award has a mathematical paper, the practice and preparatory work you undertake in advance of this examination should provide you with valid evidence for the calculation section of the key skills unit.

Geography A-level

About the syllabus
The Geography awards encourage students to acquire and apply knowledge and understanding of physical and human processes, develop an understanding of the interrelationships between people and their environments, appreciate the dynamic nature of the subject and understand how to use and manage resources and environments.

There are aspects of the geography courses that are particularly useful for generating number evidence. These involve:

- Carrying out investigative work, based on evidence from primary sources, including fieldwork, and evidence from secondary sources.
- Identifying, selecting and collecting quantitative and qualitative evidence from a range of sources.
- Working on physical and human processes.
- Working on your internal assessment, which in some courses can be up to 30% of the assessment. Evidence includes maps at a variety of scales and also statistical data. It has to be presented in cartographic and diagrammatic form. This will mean analysing and evaluating and

interpreting it then drawing conclusions as well as evaluating your methods and approaches to enquiry, explaining the limitations of the evidence and drawing valid conclusions. Remember that any fieldwork or investigations you do will potentially count as a *substantial and complex* activity asked for in the number key skill. Course work in geography normally looks to mark you on data collection, data presentation and your graphical presentation techniques, analysis and interpretation, and your ability to draw conclusions and evaluate the work. These are all very closely related to the number key skill requirements.

You will be assessed on your ability to gather, interpret, use and present information, a great deal of which is likely to involve numbers. So the key skill will be able to support you in this, and your geography course will naturally generate number evidence.

Opportunities to generate evidence
The opportunities for generating number evidence from your geography course really depend on the topics you are studying. The following list tries to identify areas of the geography syllabus that have good opportunities to generate some number evidence. Even if you are not studying the particular topics listed below, you should take time to look at them to get useful ideas. Brackets are used to show aspects of the number key skill specifications.

- **Planning an activity**
  Fieldwork
- **Interpreting information**
  Tabulated data
  Using topographical maps (especially OS 1:25 000 and 1:50 000)
  Other map types (e.g. land use and sketch maps)
  Cartographic map forms (isoline, choropleth, kite diagrams, etc.)
  Line graphs (including log/semi log scales) and cumulative line graphs
  Bar charts and histograms
  Pie charts
  Scatter graphs (establishing dispersion and best fit) and triangular graphs
  Sketch sections, cross-sections and long sections
  Proportional symbols
  Working with spatial and temporal scales
- **Working with primary sources of information**
  Sketching
  Taking field measurements
  Field mapping
- **Working with secondary sources**
  Census returns
  OS maps
  Other published statistics. If you are looking at changing landforms and focusing on rivers then get river flow information from water

See also: **Travel and Tourism Vocational A-level**, page 121

companies, newspaper flood reports, local archive material and EA statistics of things like coastal erosion

- **Carrying out calculations using**
  Scales and proportions (scales and proportions)
  Normal distributions (statistics)
  Mean, mode, median (statistics)
  Standard deviation (formula)
  Quartiles and interquartile ranges (statistics)
  Spearman rank correlation
  Chi-squared tests (formula)
  Cost-benefit analysis
- **Interpreting results and presenting your findings**

When creating any of the different types of information, charts, graphs or diagrams listed above in the interpreting information section just make sure you:

- Justify your choice of methods.
- Use the appropriate conventions.
- Draw appropriate conclusions.
- Acknowledge how possible sources of error could influence your results, where this is appropriate.

What you must know
Part 1: The Learning Curve will help you with the knowledge you need.

What you must do
Part 2: The Bottom Line will help you with the evidence you need

General opportunities for evidence

- Working with population figures, distributions and density; for example working with patterns of health using rates per 1000 of different diseases and using census figures.
- Working with economic factors and measuring development and disparity (e.g. using GDP, HDI); working with trade figures.
- Working with indicators of economic activity; for example, techniques like the location quotient and Lorenz curve drawn from employment statistics; growth and employment trends, balance of payments.

History A-level

About the syllabus

The History awards encourage students to acquire and communicate knowledge and understanding of selected periods of history. You will also develop an understanding of historical terms and concepts and explore the significance of events, individuals, issues and societies in history.

Application of Number is perhaps the most difficult of all the key skills to generate evidence for in history courses. It is extremely unlikely that you will get an opportunity to develop most of your number portfolio from just your History course, so you need to look elsewhere too. This means that you must have a properly organised portfolio, carefully tracking where your evidence came from and what it covers in the key skill.

There are three aspects of the history course that could be used to generate number evidence relatively easily:

- Working on historical evidence and the methods used by historians in analysis and evaluation.
- Analysing, evaluating, interpreting and using historical sources of different kinds.
- Doing course work or internal assessment. In some history courses the internal assessment component can be up to 30%. This can give you an opportunity to work more closely with numbers to help support your history work.

Opportunities for evidence

The opportunities for generating number evidence from your history course really depend on the topics you are studying. The following sections try to identify areas of the history syllabus that have good opportunities to generate some number evidence. Even if you are not studying the particular topics listed below, you should take time to look at them to get useful ideas.

Topic area 1
US themes

Economy and society in the USA 1919–33

Looking at the impact of the First World War, Henry Ford and new mass production methods may provide an opportunity to read and understand scale drawings, graphs, complex tables and charts. There may also be opportunities to show that you can work comfortably with very large numbers.

The same type of number opportunities will occur if you study the causes and consequences of the Wall Street crash. You may also be able to carry out multi-step calculations with numbers to find the rates of growth and slump in key markets. As a related activity, you could show changes of proportions. For Wall Street crash work you might be working with graphs and charts, try to work out how you could represent data and figures to meet different purposes or convert them into different types of graphical information.

FDR and the New Deal in the USA

The nature of the New Deal and, more specifically, policies to deal with agriculture, industry, unemployment and welfare could mean handling statistics. You may have to show you can obtain information from different sources and use this information to explain historical contexts, concepts or issues (all acceptable purposes for using number). You could also select and use appropriate graphical methods to illustrate your findings, show trends or make comparisons. This might involve finding new and more effective ways to represent number information to better prove points that you want to make. This will allow you to examine critically and justify your choice of methods.

The same types of opportunities also exist when you look at the extent of recovery and success of the New Deal to 1945. Perhaps here you will be able to draw comparisons, looking at growth in relation to other countries. This will allow you to generate different types of number evidence as you try to establish how best to do this.

Civil rights in the USA 1945–68

Opportunities here are probably limited to population numbers, percentages and distributions and comparisons of health, welfare and income. Over the time period there may be opportunities to show trends and changes in participation rates, employment patterns and changes in income and health. All the time these numbers can be shown comparatively by looking at the patterns which exist in the white US population. This will provide you with opportunities to construct and label charts, graphs and diagrams using accepted conventions and to justify your methods and draw appropriate conclusions from your findings.

Topic area 2
German themes

Bismarck and the Unification of Germany 1848–71

By looking at the economic factors favouring unification, you will be dealing with numbers. Depending on the nature of your studies you may find opportunities to interpret, calculate and present numbers in different ways. There may also be scope for comparative work, which can mean generating your own methods of presenting appropriate statistics.

Weimar Germany 1918–29

The economy and in particular reparation and hyperinflation will mean working with numbers. You may have the opportunity to calculate and chart growth and inflation, drawing comparisons. You might also do your own investigations obtain relevant information from different sources and use it to meet a particular task (purpose). There will certainly be the opportunity to present your statistics and data on this period in appropriate graphical ways and then to draw conclusions and justify your methods.

Hitler's Germany 1933–39

When looking at Nazi economic solutions, and the construction and industrial production, work programmes and rearmament, perhaps even the social impact of Nazism on classes and the role and status of women, there will be a range of opportunities to generate number evidence. The approaches mentioned in the Weimar period can probably be used here too. A useful way of getting particular points across is to make comparisons with what was happening in other countries. It is also a great way of generating your own number evidence.

Topic area 3
UK Themes

The impact of industrialisation in Britain 1780–1914
In particular, the size and distribution of the population change will provide some opportunities to generate number evidence.

The Railway Age 1830–1914
The economic impact of railways in terms of industry, private investment and food supplies can all generate number evidence. You may have to obtain relevant information to meet a specific purpose, handle large numbers, make comparisons, draw conclusions, determine the rate of growth or calculate proportional change. The social impact of the railways will mean looking at cities, holidays and leisure. This could mean interpreting and calculating and presenting statistics.

Other UK themes
Whenever you tackle a theme, look for opportunities to demonstrate these skills:

- Actively carry out your own research.
- Obtain relevant number information.
- Show you can interpret graphs, complex tables and charts.
- handle large numbers
- Work out rates of change and make appropriate comparisons.
- Present your number evidence in the most effective way to back up your arguments.

Here are some other themes:

- **Representation and democracy 1830–1931:** Particularly when looking at changes to the size and composition of the electorate.
- **The age of Lord Liverpool 1815–27:** In particular, when learning about trade and finance.
- **Public health and social policy 1832–75:** Look for the statistics related to costs, participation rates etc.
- **British society 1919–1939:** In particular, statistics and data related to the depression and unemployment between the wars. Other potential areas to generate number information might be when looking at government responses to the problem of unemployment. Also, looking at the living standards and regional and social differences may mean further opportunities to generate number evidence.

Topic area 4
Life in the USSR 1928–41

The collectivisation of agriculture and its impact will involve rates of growth, percentage changes and the potential to draw comparisons; as will studying industrialisation and its impact.

Topic area 5
War themes

There could be the opportunity to work with a number of different types of statistics and comparative figures, graphs and charts. You may even be able to establish different ways of presenting data to illustrate particular points that you would like to make.

- **Europe at war 1939–45**: Should generate a range of different comparative statistics.
- **Cold war and détente**: Particularly when looking at NATO and Warsaw Pact weapon, troop and expenditure comparisons. There is also the Marshall Plan as another potential source of number evidence.

General opportunities to look for

- Working with population figures, distributions and density.
- Working with economic factors like growth, balance of payments, inflation and unemployment.
- Working with maps and scale drawings.
- Gauging indications of wealth by comparative standards and by current UK standards. With all work looking at non-UK countries, there is always the opportunity to convert between currencies, though remember this will mean establishing what the equivalencies were then before translating them into current equivalencies. This is of course a multi-stage calculation (just like the key skill asks for) but it depends on you obtaining relevant information from different sources. Not a bad idea for a substantial and complex activity with a clear purpose (just like the key skill asks for!).

What you must know
Part 1: The Learning Curve will help you with the knowledge you need.

What you must do
Part 2: The Bottom Line will help you with the evidence you need

Mathematics A-level

About the syllabus

The Mathematics award aims to help you develop your understanding of mathematics and mathematical processes in a way that develops your capability and confidence. The ability to reason logically and to generalise will help you to recognise how problems, tasks and situations can be represented mathematically and then resolved, refined or improved. You will be expected to extend your range of mathematical skills and techniques and apply them in increasingly challenging contexts as well as recognising coherence and progression across and within the subject. The ability to choose appropriate mathematical skills and techniques and apply them to real-world problems is where your mathematical studies overlap with the key skill of Application of Number.

Topic area 1
Application of mathematics

Planning and interpreting information

You will be expected to develop planning skills that will require you to recall, select and use your mathematical knowledge to represent real situations. This will involve planning a substantial and complex activity by breaking it down into a series of tasks. The most likely opportunities for this will be found in class work or course work that addresses mechanics or decision mathematics.

As well as using your existing knowledge you must also obtain relevant information from different sources. This information may come from direct observation and experimentation or from the investigation and research of secondary sources such as the internet, CD-ROMs or other relevant data. You will also be expected to identify appropriate formulas, methods and techniques that will enable you to obtain the results you need.

The skills identified above are central to the requirement for mathematics programmes to address at least one area of the application of mathematics as well as for the key skill. You should use the accuracy and quality of your record keeping to demonstrate how, when and why you made decisions. This is an important dimension of the key skill that must be made explicit.

Calculating

The extent to which the specific multi-step calculations are demonstrated will depend upon the focus of your task. You must ensure that all methods and calculations are clearly and logically set out with answers given using appropriate levels of accuracy and correct units of measurement. All calculations must be checked for accuracy and errors in procedures.

Interpreting results and presenting findings

Interpreting and presenting your results, and explaining how they represent a satisfactory solution to the original task or problem, are central to the key skill at this level. If you are required to compare experimental results with established expectations you will need to explain your understanding of inconsistencies in the two sets of data and the means by which they can be effectively addressed in the future. Your presentation must also use established graphical methods – graphs, charts and diagrams – to ensure that the key skill requirements are met.

Topic area 2
Statistics

Planning and interpreting information

The extent to which you will need to obtain relevant information will depend upon the nature and context of your task. Class work is likely to provide you with immediate access to data whereas course work and proj-

ects will require you to undertake data collection. Data collection may come from direct observation, experimentation, questionnaires, simulation, or from secondary sources. You will be expected to work with a large data set (over 50 items) and choose appropriate methods for collection, analysis and representation. Retain evidence of making accurate and reliable observations, using suitable equipment and recording using appropriate units.

Calculating

The handling of statistics is a central requirement of the key skill. You will be expected to manipulate your data and undertake statistical calculations involving distribution, mean and median. You will be expected to represent your data graphically using frequency tables, histograms and other graphs. All calculations and use of formulae will need to be carefully checked, and where errors are found, the source identified and the results corrected.

Interpreting results and presenting findings

You will be expected to interpret, explain, evaluate and communicate your conclusions. This should be done using graphical representation and must always refer back to the original task or problem. Remember that the use of statistics here is to demonstrate your understanding of how they can tackle real-world situations.

To meet the requirements of the key skill, your presentation may be oral with graphical stimuli, or a written report including graphs, charts and diagrams. The extent to which this matches your mathematical studies will depend upon the structure of your course and the requirements of the examining body.

Further opportunities for evidence

The Mathematics A-level has an expectation that you will have achieved at least a grade C at GCSE and this assumes that you have a detailed background knowledge of the fundamentals of mathematics which will not be examined. However, the key skill requires you to demonstrate an ability to work with multi-stage calculations on amounts and sizes, scales and proportion, handling statistics and rearranging and using formulas. All aspects of your class work and course work should provide examples of your ability to work clearly, accurately and to check your working methods and results. You are advised to collect examples of this ability in order to demonstrate and record your coverage of this aspect of the key skills.

The statistics and applied aspects of your mathematics studies may also offer you the opportunity to generate data or identify an experiment or situation that arises from another programme of study. The combination of work from different contexts is a further example of your ability to apply the key skill.

What you must know
Part 1: The Learning Curve will help you with the knowledge you need.

What you must do
Part 2: The Bottom Line will help you with the evidence you need

Physics A-level

About the syllabus

The Physics awards aim to develop essential knowledge and understanding in physics and, where appropriate, how physics is applied. They will also help you develop a connection between theory and experiment an appreciation of how physics is used, and an idea of how it has developed to the present day.

Topic area 1
Working on your experimental skills

See also: **Science Vocational A-level**, page 119

Planning and interpreting information

You will be required to develop planning skills. This will involve making predictions; selecting parameters, equipment, procedures and methods; and working with your observations. In executing your experiments, you will be asked to use apparatus correctly to make observations to a required degree of accuracy. This will also include being able to check the operation of apparatus, choosing appropriate scales and ranges for instruments.

Measuring skills that you will use in experimental work will involve using appropriate techniques and recognising the effect of any measuring equipment on the measurements. You will also be using SI base units as well as other relevant units. In developing these skills you will have an opportunity to obtain relevant information from different sources, using it to meet a clear purpose and to make accurate and reliable observations and using suitable equipment to measure in a variety of appropriate units.

All of these skills will generate evidence for your Application of Number key skill, and you should ensure that in performing and developing these skills you have a reliable and clear way of recording your experimental work for your key skills portfolio.

Calculating

Experimental work and the related skill development will also involve analysis and developing your analytical abilities. This will also give you a chance to develop evidence for the calculation section of the number key skill.

Your physics course will teach you to use arithmetical and graphical techniques to process observations that you make using a variety of mathematical techniques.

You may also learn about the uncertainty in an experimental result by considering uncertainties in any individual measurements taken. This will provide a chance to collect evidence for showing how your methods work with appropriate levels of accuracy and to show how you can check your method and procedures to identify errors in methods and results.

Depending on the experiments done and measurements taken, you will

Opportunities

certainly have the opportunity to rearrange and use formulas, equations and expressions.

Interpreting results and presenting findings

In your analysis work you will study your data to draw conclusions and make sensible comment on the reliability of your conclusions. This will give you an opportunity to collect evidence for your number portfolio to show you can draw appropriate conclusions based on your findings, including how possible sources of error might have affected your results.

In developing your experimenting skills you will focus on presentation. This will involve developing the skills involved in constructing schematic diagrams of apparatus and presenting clear recordings of experiments. You will also have an opportunity to learn how to tabulate observations, draw neat graphs and present appropriate conclusions. This will mean learning how to use appropriate significant figures and units.

This should provide ample opportunities to generate number evidence that shows you could select and use appropriate methods to illustrate your findings. You will also generate evidence showing that you can construct and label charts, graphs, diagrams and scale drawings using appropriate conventions. In writing up your experimental work, you will draw up appropriate conclusions based on your findings, including how possible sources of error might have affected your results.

Reflecting on your results and experimental findings will also help you explain how they relate to the purpose of your experiments or experimental activity.

Topic area 2
Preparing for your practical examinations

Practical examinations will try to determine how well you can carry out various experiments. In practising for this part of your course you will have the opportunity to develop a range of skills and evidence that can be used as evidence for your number key skill.

The basic framework for experimenting that you will be expected to learn and develop has a clear relationship to the Application of Number key skill requirements. The relevant Application of Number sections are shown in brackets. You will be developing the ability to:

- Plan experiments: identify variables, make reasonable predictions of the expected outcome, and identify suitable equipment and procedures (planning an activity and interpreting information).
- Make appropriate measurements (planning an activity and interpreting information.)
- Analyse data (carrying out calculations).
- Present data in an appropriate form (interpreting results and presenting your findings.)
- Tabulate data appropriately (interpreting results and presenting your findings.)

- Present data using appropriate graphical methods (interpreting results and presenting your findings).
- Make deductions and draw sensible conclusions from graphical data (interpreting results and presenting your findings).

Further opportunities for evidence

The following areas of study may also prove to be useful in generating Application of Number evidence. There is a level of mathematical competence required of students taking courses in physics. This will provide a clear opportunity to show that you are capable of meeting the key skill requirements. In particular, look out for the following areas:

- **Arithmetic and computation**: where you will be expected to recognise and use expressions in decimal and standard form. You will also be expected to show that you can use ratios, fractions and percentages; use calculators to find x^n, $1/x$, $\sqrt{x}$, $\log_{10} x$, e^x
- **Handling data**: showing you can make magnitude calculations; use an appropriate number of significant figures; find arithmetic means.
- **Geometry and trigonometry**: showing you can calculate areas of triangles, circumferences and areas of circles, surface areas and volumes of rectangular blocks, cylinders and spheres. You should also be able to use Pythagoras' theorem; use the sum of a triangle; show you have the ability to use sines, cosines and tangents in physical problems; understand the relationship between degrees and radians and translate from one to another.
- **Graphs**: among other things, you will be expected to show you can translate information between graphical, numerical and algebraic forms and plot two variables from experimental or other data.

You should also look for opportunities in the following areas of study:

- **Momentum and energy**: in particular momentum concepts and $p = mv$, energy concepts
- **Electricity**: in particular electromotive force, and potential difference, resistance and DC circuits.

Remember there will be several different formulas that you will encounter as you learn about the relationships between different quantities.

Evidence from Vocational A-level courses

Art and Design Vocational A-level

About the specifications

The Art and Design award includes the study of topics like working with materials; developing, exploring and recording your use of visual language; investigating, exploring and recording others' use of visual language; working with materials; techniques and technology and working to set briefs. It includes course work and personal investigation and presentation of work. Remember that these topics will help you generate Application of Number evidence. Your use of number skills may also help to improve your art and design.

See also: **Art A-level**, page 54

Topic area 1
Developing, exploring and recording visual language

Planning and interpreting information

Investigation, exploration and interpretation are key activities in developing your 2D and 3D visual language. Before you are able to explore and interpret effectively you will need to have a clear understanding of what you are doing and what your starting point is. This will involve:

- Planning carefully, including time for exploration and skill, development, as well as making sure deadlines and schedules are met.
- Preparing carefully, making sure you have carried out all the relevant research and collected all the information you need in the form of data, ideas, measurements or drawings and diagrams.
- Estimating accurately to ensure that wherever possible you have sufficient media and materials plus access to equipment and technology to help you develop and realise your ideas.

Calculating

When developing and exploring 2D and 3D visual language it is likely that you will investigate ideas and try out techniques in test pieces, swatches, samples, maquettes or models before moving on to the larger finished pieces where all your investigations, explorations and interpretations are brought together.

As ideas move towards the final outcome it is likely that you will have to use a range of calculations to do with:

- Amounts and sizes as you work out the media and materials you need access to.
- Scales and proportion as you decide on the size of your finished work in relation to the media and materials used in your preparatory work.

If you are working with more technologically based work like screen printing you may also have the opportunity to work with statistics or formulas.

Interpreting results and presenting findings

Presenting art, craft and design work is a natural part of the process of creative development. It is particularly relevant in project work that is large-scale in terms of size. This size may refer to:

- Actual size of the final artefact
- Batch size in terms of number of items
- Size of the media and materials budget

Working scale drawings provide an ideal vehicle for presenting both your development work and your final outcome. Always ensure that scale drawings use the accepted conventions of labelling, recording and stating scales. A range of working drawings which show your thinking and record any associated calculations can provide excellent evidence of the role of number and your use of it.

Topic area 2
Investigating, exploring and recording others' use of visual language and professional practice

Planning and interpreting information

A central theme of the award is an appreciation and awareness of historical and contemporary practice in art, craft and design. When exploring historical and contemporary references as well as professional practice you will have the opportunity to:

- Collect and interpret relevant information on the artist, craftsperson or designer.
- Explore and interpret their work paying particular attention to the role of number in their practice either as an essential part of their creativity or as a central skill when dealing with costs or time constraints.
- Develop and apply your own numerical skills as you respond to and record the work of other artists, craftspeople and designers.

In addition to collecting and interpreting information, you need to show

Opportunities

how you have planned your research by breaking it down into a series of tasks.

Remember that you will also be expected to show evidence of having used a range of different sources. Valuable observations can be made using drawings or photography but ensure their scale and proportion are made clear using accurate and relevant measurements.

Calculating

Professional practice requires a clear understanding of markets, outlets and production costs. This is as true for the successful fine artist as it is for the craftsperson and the designer. This topic provides you with an opportunity to explore the multi-stage and compound costs of professional practice by:

- Calculating the development, design, production and presentation costs of a named individual's work. This will enable you to explore costs associated with unique or batch production, exhibition costs including transport, framing or packaging as well as catalogues and publicity.
- Calculating your own comparable practice which has been informed by your research on others' professional practice.

Interpreting results and presenting findings

Your findings on the cost implications of professional practice and comparison between the demands of a recognised artist, craftsperson or designer with your own personal development and projects, this should provide good source material for you to make a critical examination and presentation.

Your evidence should be presented using tables, charts and diagrams to show how industrial comparisons have been made. It is important that you make clear where you have made assumptions if accurate information was not available, and show how your assumptions could lead to possible sources of error and affect your results.

Topic area 3
Working to set briefs in art, craft or design

Planning and interpreting information

A set brief is the typical approach to commissioning an artist, craftsperson or designer. A brief will be precise and will identify:

- What the client wants
- The media and materials favoured
- The constraints imposed, usually time limit and costs
- The consultation process

The brief will be your first point of information but you will need to consult other sources. This may require:

- Survey of a site or location.
- Consulting the target audience or potential users.
- Estimating the development time and the realisation time needed.
- Exploring similar projects or outcomes and how they were achieved through visits, scale drawings and other records.
- A detailed plan of stages of development, including consultation process and discussion and review with the client.

Calculating

Realising any project from a brief will require a range of calculations that will firm up your original estimates during the planning stage. These will include calculations to do with:

- Amounts and sizes of materials needed.
- Scales and proportion of original ideas and drawings in relation to the final outcome.
- Statistical analysis of any investigations or consultation regarding the views of others.
- Using formulas where specialist glues, chemicals or materials are used; scaling up batches or areas and volumes of shapes and spares.

Scaling up and using proportions may need you to convert from one measure to another. Make sure you keep records of these conversions. Professional artists, craftspeople and designers are very precise when calculating and they keep detailed, logical and clear records of all processes and procedures. As part of your developing practice, ensure that you do the same and remember to keep evidence of your calculations as the creative aspect takes over.

Interpreting results and presenting findings

The client will expect clear presentation of project costs and market, plus consumer or audience information to support your work in responding to the brief. In the professional world these are as important as the visual outcome itself. Without an effective presentation and a careful explanation of the basis of your calculations and their outcome, a commission may be lost.

Always support your final ideas with other graphical displays. Consumer or audience statistics can be displayed using a pie chart. Development and production costs can be clearly set out in a table. Always show how your work has a built-in margin for error. It is better for you to point this out than for the client to point it out to you later.

Opportunities from optional units

Units with art applications

Collecting information from a variety of sources to help you plan, prepare and begin working in painting, drawing, collage, printmaking, sculpture or installations will require you to explore specialist documents on the skills or techniques associated with these areas. These documents are likely

to have information stored in graphs, tables, charts and diagrams that you will need to read and understand them.

A variety of simple and complex calculations will be associated with each skill. The extent to which you use them will depend upon the work you undertake. Always try to calculate as well as estimate. Not only will this develop your skill and improve your accuracy, it will also develop your confidence in the importance of number in art.

Units with craft applications

Like the art units, you will have the opportunity to search for information and data from a variety of sources as you develop your ideas and produce finished work. Calculations in craft are usually associated with timing and batch production. This ranges from kiln firing and glaze quality in ceramics to the costs associated with producing and selling items of jewellery or other short-run artefacts.

Units with design applications

There are several types of design: graphics, 3D, surface and textile are perhaps the most common. Each has a range of media, materials and techniques which are relevant to the particular area, and each has a range of technical information and data which will need to be known and understood before undertaking a project in this area.

Calculations will be similar to those associated with art and craft, although they vary according to special areas and will include:

- Amounts and sizes when working on 3D designs for furniture.
- Scales and proportion from graphic and surface design.
- Using formulas for dyes and chemicals in textile and graphic (photo-based) design.

What you must know
Part 1: The Learning Curve will help you with the knowledge you need.

What you must do
Part 2: The Bottom Line will help you with the evidence you need

Business Vocational A-level

About the specifications

The GNVQ Business course includes the study of topics like marketing, business planning and finance.

See also: **Business A-level**, page 59

Topic area 1
Marketing

Planning and interpreting information

The creation of a marketing strategy will be one clear opportunity to plan a substantial and complex activity by breaking it down into a series of tasks. If you choose to do this, group your various tasks clearly and logically, perhaps organising logical time frames. You might be able to conduct primary research (surveys, use of sampling, pilots and field trials). Secondary research data will be another source of numerical information.

Working with marketing databases might be a useful way to show you can work with a large set of data (over 50 items). Ensure your interrogation of databases is purposeful and helps you to meet your goals. The key skill asks you to ensure that you use large data sets to meet the purpose of your activity. Databases can provide information about customer behaviour – customer preferences and buying patterns, sales trends for new and existing products, product substitution. All these things may involve interpreting numerical information. They may also contain numerical information about the market, e.g. market share, market segments and competitor activities.

In identifying, collecting and using primary and secondary data, there will be clear opportunities to get involved with planning and interpreting information from different sources. This may also include large data sets of over 50 items. A large data set could be published data or it could be data you have generated yourself. Databases and secondary sources may present numerical information using graphs, complex tables and charts.

Calculating

Pricing and the techniques of pricing – penetration, skimming, cost plus and the difference between value and price – may involve multi-step calculations. There will also be opportunities to show your methods clearly and to use appropriate levels of accuracy.

Larger data sets may involve using measures of average and range to compare distributions, and to estimate mean, median and range of grouped data. Working with primary and secondary data will provide opportunities to use checking procedures that identify errors in your methods and the results they generate.

You may need to look at the information collected and predict the possibilities for growth in sales, forecast percentage increases, and consider various possibilities and scenarios.

Interpreting results and presenting findings

The marketing strategy can be written up using graphical methods to support the points made and to enhance the overall impact and effect of the proposals. You could also use graphical methods of presenting information during any oral presentation of your strategy. When interpreting numerical information from other sources, look at how the source presents it then decide how you might modify the presentation for your purpose.

Topic area 2
Finance

Planning and interpreting information

Financial reports are based on a range of documents used to control financial activities. Different stakeholders use financial ratios to assist them in interpreting accounts and in making judgements about the effectiveness of business. You may have an opportunity to work with these figures or even to generate your own. Using annual reports from businesses

will mean having to learn how to interpret financial information in order to make calculations using financial ratios.

Looking at the financial performance of a business, using a range of financial data (including information from ratios and shareholder returns) and then drawing conclusions from your findings, this is one exercise that would take you through all three aspects of the key skill (a substantial and complex activity). It may also be a useful way of revising for your assessment.

Calculating

When practising how to measure business financial performance, you will be able to show that you can use formulas and data, thus generating evidence that can be used for your key skill portfolio.

In creating and maintaining accurate financial records, there will be opportunities to generate evidence to show that you can interpret information, make necessary calculations and work out clear ways of presenting your work.

Constructing simple accounts, simple balance sheets and profit and loss accounts will mean having to understand and work with:

- Costs and revenue
- Purchases and sales of stock
- Creditors and debtors
- Fixed and current assets

Recording this financial information and the accounting flow will provide opportunities for gathering evidence. There will also be opportunities when working with manual and computerised accounting methods.

You will need to know how to use the following performance, solvency and profitability ratios and be able to use them to make appropriate financial calculations:

- Return on capital employed
- Profit margin ratios
- Asset turnover
- Stock turnover
- Selling and debt collection period
- Current ratio
- Acid test ratio

Financial performance can be measured by assessing shareholder returns using the following indicators: share prices, dividends, price/earnings ratios.

Learning about financial management means interpreting and working with budgets and cash flow. You will also need to understand variance analysis. There may also be an opportunity to collect key skill evidence when you study working capital.

Interpreting results and presenting findings

Knowing the limitations of ratio analysis will be important for both your

See also: **Retail and Distributive Services Vocational A-level**, page 116

business course and the number key skill. The number key skill asks you to examine critically the methods you use and also to show an awareness of possible sources of error and the effects they might have.

You may have to depict trends or make comparisons, show performance (e.g. share price) or even work out how best to present complex financial information for business reports. These opportunities will show that you can chose appropriate methods, construct appropriate charts, graphs, diagrams and tables, and to use labels and accepted conventions appropriately and effectively.

Topic area 3
Business planning

Planning and interpreting information
Market analysis and planning can involve working with primary and secondary research data to undertake market research. Analysing this type of data is one way to ensure you make informed judgements about the likely sales levels of a product. Both primary and secondary data can involve working with numbers and will provide opportunities to show you can interpret numerical information.

Calculating
Financial analysis and planning can involve working with budgets including information about start-up and working capital. It can also involve undertaking break-even forecasts and simple cash flow forecasts. There may also be an opportunity to produce projected profit and loss accounts and start-up balance sheets.

Interpreting results and presenting findings
There may also be opportunities to evaluate your business plan, looking at the return on capital employed, profit margins and the percentage of market share gained. In evaluating your financial plan you may need to show you can reflect on the financial viability of your plan.

In producing your financial and business plans you will have the opportunity to show that you can present numerical information graphically and that you are able to chose suitable methods to do so. You will be expected to use a range of formats to increase the clarity and directness of your plan.

What you must know
Part 1: The Learning Curve will help you with the knowledge you need.

What you must do
Part 2: The Bottom Line will help you with the evidence you need

Construction and the Built Environment Vocational A-level

About the specifications
The units of the Construction and Built Environment award include the study of towns and cities that make up the environment including their buildings and the civil engineering structures of their infrastructure.

Opportunities

The study includes the technology and performance of structures, of buildings, and of services within buildings such as water supplies and energy supplies. Common to all these studies are the ideas of investigating, surveying, measuring, design and reporting results.

Optional units continue studies in the pathways of architecture and design, building, civil engineering, building services engineering, town planning and development.

Topic areas
Investigating the environment
Evaluations and surveys
Design procedures
Performance of materials, structures and services

Planning and interpreting information

The investigation of environments, on the scale of a town or a building, or in the detail of a building's services, often starts with planning your visit and interpreting sources. You need to break the proposed activity into a number of tasks and the following types of activity will produce evidence for the key skill:

- Selecting and interpreting maps, plans and technical drawings.
- Using paper-based and computer-based information systems.
- Identifying, measuring and recording significant positions and areas.
- Making observations and using measuring equipment.

The processes of design for towns, structures, buildings and services require you to plan your activities and to interpret many sources. Design decisions are also informed by a technical knowledge about particular materials or other choices of technology. Here are some typical activities relevant to the key skill:

- Interpreting client requirements.
- Selecting and interpreting maps, plans and technical drawings.
- Using paper-based and computer-based information systems.
- Interpreting data and making appropriate selections.

In carrying out these activities you will have opportunities to gather data from different sources, to handle very small or very large numbers, to use estimation for numbers, and to record results in appropriate units.

Calculating

To make use of your results from field observations, measurements and data collection you need to carry out calculation. Here are some possible areas of activity connected to the key skill:

- Calculating areas of compound shapes such as plots of land, roads, sections through hills, buildings, building components and service ducts.
- Calculating volumes of shapes such as earth mounds or trenches, buildings, rooms, pipes and ducts.

- Processing statistical results from large data sets, such as population trends in towns and performance of components.
- Working with ratios and scales in interpreting results and in presenting your findings.
- Using energy formulas involving areas, temperatures and insulation values.

These activities will lead you to meeting the requirements of the key skill such as in knowing how to use formulas and other techniques for finding areas and volumes and for solving triangles. You need to know about possible sources of error in your methods and your results. Pay attention to possible sources of error in the measurements, such as the natural errors in instruments and in your methods of using them.

Interpreting results and presenting findings

You will need to present the results of your investigations and you should have a good choice of opportunities to illustrate your findings, to show trends and to make comparisons. Here are some typical activities:

- Using maps, diagrams and drawings with appropriate labels and scales.
- Presenting statistical data, trends and other results using charts and graphs.
- Choosing findings you wish to highlight and selecting appropriate graphical methods to do this.

Equally as important as the presentation of your findings are drawing appropriate conclusions based on your findings and relating them to the purpose of your investigation. You also need to be able to evaluate and justify the methods you have used. Did they produce useful results? Are there better methods?

Opportunities from optional units

Projects for town development and construction involve many aspects of finance such as mechanisms for raising money, estimating costs and tracking the flow of money. Some optional units include analysis of financial aspects; they provide good evidence for the key skill. Construction firms are among the larger companies listed on the stock market; tracking and analysing their performance is another good area for evidence. Look at page 145 to see examples of evidence available from the finance pages in newspapers.

What you must know
Part 1: The Learning Curve will help you with the knowledge you need.

What you must do
Part 2: The Bottom Line will help you with the evidence you need

Opportunities

Engineering Vocational A-level

About the specifications
The Engineering award includes a study of the links between engineering organisations and business, finance, the economy and the environment.

The award also includes units where engineering is investigated by applying principles of design, materials technology, science and mathematics. Optional units give you the opportunity to continue studies in particular pathways such as electrical engineering, mechanical engineering, telecommunications and automotive engineering.

See also: **Design and technology A-level**, page 67

Topic area 1
Investigating engineering organisations

Planning and interpreting information

In carrying out case studies of an engineering organisation you will be using written, numerical and graphical data of various types relating to engineering activities within the organisation, and the various relationships and links within the organisation. Some of the information will involve large data sets such as financial and economic reports.

You will need to plan what aspect of production or service you are going to study and select appropriate data for calculation and for presentation. Remember to keep evidence to show that you were able to select and interpret information to help your investigations.

Calculating

In describing the economic contributions of organisations you are likely to be analysing company accounts and analysing statistical data associated with the local economy and the national economy. You will also need to convert information to quantities, percentages and other comparisons that are effective. Your investigation will involve financial decisions taken about one aspect of production or service provision, with a record of the calculations used in making the decision. These calculations are likely to involve financial formulas such as those associated with costs, profits and return on capital. Remember to keep records of these calculations.

Interpreting results and presenting findings

The results of your investigations into aspects of engineering organisations will require a variety of techniques to interpret them and to present them. The key skill requirement for a graph, a chart and a diagram should be easy to meet. Opportunities include showing:

- Structure and functions of an organisation.
- Links between engineering activities and commercial activities.
- Information flow between parts of an organisation.

Topic area 2
Performance and design of engineering products and services

Planning and interpreting information

A number of units in the Vocational A-level involve investigations into the performance and the design of chosen engineering products or services. You will therefore encounter a variety of information and techniques such as the following:

- Assessing the properties and effect on product performance of materials by using measurements, test data and secondary sources.
- Using technical and marketing data from manufacturers and suppliers to assist their practical investigations of new technology.
- Undertaking practical investigations into the operation of the product or service.
- Investigating electrical and mechanical engineering products which involve motion and electricity.
- Undertaking developmental work for design proposals, interpreting numerical information taken from a design brief and the related drawings.

You need to plan efficient techniques for your purpose and you should be able to interpret the information gained perhaps by correctly understanding relationships and units.

Calculating

To make use of your information from measurements and data collection you often need to carry out calculations, such as the following:

- Using formulas to predict values for energy, electrical and mechanical applications.
- Calculating quantities, dimensions and shapes of materials and components required for the product or service.
- Carrying out calculations on amounts and sizes by using and rearranging formulas.
- Carrying out multi-step calculations on scales and proportions by using appropriate conventions, standards and projections.

Interpreting results and presenting findings

You will need to present the results of your investigations and you should have a good choice of opportunities to illustrate your findings, to show trends and to make comparisons. Typical opportunities include the following:

- Choosing findings you wish to highlight and selecting appropriate graphical methods to do this.
- Using, graphs, charts, diagrams and drawings with appropriate labels and scales.
- Setting out the materials and dimensions of components needed to make the product or the component.
- Using data to present and explain mechanical and electrical features such as motion or energy efficiency.
- Producing a final design solution accompanied by drawings.

Equally as important as the presentation of your findings are drawing appropriate conclusions based on your findings and relating them to the purpose of your investigation. You also need to be able evaluate and justify the methods that you used. Did they produce useful results. Are there better methods it?

What you must know
Part 1: The Learning Curve will help you with the knowledge you need.

What you must do
Part 2: The Bottom Line will help you with the evidence you need

Opportunities

Health and Social Care Vocational A-level

About the specifications

The Health and Social Care awards include the study of topics like physical aspects of health, research perspectives in health and social care and epidemiology. Epidemiology may not occur as a unit in its own right, but it will be a feature of several different units.

Topic area 1
Physical aspects of health

Planning and interpreting information

You are likely to be involved in taking physiological measurements of people in care settings. This is likely to involve:

- Making routine observations.
- Taking and recording physiological measurements for people.
- Establishing expected range and deviations from the range for these people.

Routine observations could be pulse, temperature, blood pressure, peak flow. The cardiorespiratory system will be monitored using pulse rate, blood pressure, breathing rate, lung volumes and peak flow measurements. You may also get a chance to use a spirometer to measure breathing rates and lung volumes, otherwise you will be using simple apparatus consisting of a calibrated container filled with water and turned upside down in a water-filled trough. Even this method will involve using number calculations. A simple peak flow meter can be used to record peak flow measurements

You need to know the possible sources of error in the practical monitoring systems and ways of estimating and reducing these errors (the accuracy of your results). Errors may be due to the monitoring process or limitations of the monitoring equipment. This will help you generate evidence to show that you can make accurate and reliable observations and use suitable equipment to measure in appropriate units.

You will also have to make accurate interpretations of secondary source data in relation to homeostatic responses. Secondary source data could include electrocardiograph (ECG) traces, spirometer tracings, blood cell counts and tables showing electrolyte concentrations in the blood.

Remember to consider abnormal readings – data which is outside normal parameters. An erythrocyte count of 3 million per cm^3 may indicate a form of anaemia. Interpreting and understanding this means showing that you are familiar with reading and understanding ways of writing very small numbers and that you can work with compound measures.

Calculating

When providing accurate analysis of results, you will need to be able to show you can:

- Use fractions and decimals to record physiological values.
- Determine and interpret rates of change from linear and non-linear graphs, e.g. changes in breathing rate or changes in oxygen consumption.
- Use formulas perhaps to express electrolyte concentrations.

Interpreting results and presenting findings

There will be opportunities to plot graphs, e.g. to record blood glucose levels, temperature, breathing rates, changes in heart rate. This will give you a number of opportunities to show your skills of interpreting results and presenting findings.

Topic area 2
Research perspectives in health and social care

Planning and interpreting information

Like the number key skill, the vocational demands of this topic involve planning and you will be encouraged to establish a clear hypothesis (what you are trying to find out). You will also be required to read research reports and articles and critically evaluate their usefulness. This provides a great opportunity to show you can identify relevant data, collect and interpret data, and analyse results.

You will need to obtain relevant information from different sources, applying different methods for obtaining primary research data such as experiments, questionnaires, interviews and observation. You will also need to use appropriate secondary sources such as epidemiology, morbidity, standard mortality rates and demography. The primary data will provide you with an opportunity to make appropriate calculations and present your results graphically. The secondary data sources will give you a great opportunity to show you can read and understand complex tables and charts.

You will also be asked to consider issues like reliability and validity of the data collected. If you are using quantitative methods consider collecting data that will mean working with over 50 items. It is a great opportunity to cover this aspect of the key skill.

Calculating

When you read research reports and articles you need to be able to critically evaluate their usefulness and to understand how the results can be applied in health and social care. Look for opportunities to generate evidence when you work on determining what type of sample you need, its size and the effect of this on your data analysis.

You will also be asked to understand the sources of bias and inaccuracy that may occur in obtaining data. This will also be an opportunity to show you can examine data critically, justify your choice of methods and work to appropriate levels of accuracy. You will also be generating evidence to show you can identify errors in methods and results.

Interpreting results and presenting findings

When writing up your findings as a report it will be important to make sure you present your numerical data using appropriate methods which clearly impart the information to the reader and effectively support the points you are making.

You will also need to use analytical methods appropriate to the method of research you have chosen. While doing this you should justify your choice of methods in your write-up. Also be prepared to justify your choice of presentation techniques and explain how the results of your calculations and analysis relate to your purpose or original hypothesis. Though this may not be a requirement for your health and social care report, it is a requirement for the key skill.

Reflecting on your findings in terms of accuracy, critically evaluating your methods of handling numbers, using ways of minimising error, justifying your methods for presenting numerical information, and making sure your number data ties in effectively with your hypothesis, all these may help with some of the grading requirements. They will certainly help in meeting the key skill requirements.

Topic area 3
Epidemiology

Epidemiology can involve complex statistics and graphical devices to show data and prove hypotheses. Analytical and experimental studies are often supported by data in the form of complex graphs, tables and charts. This might be the first time you encounter a scatter graph.

Very often the graphical representations used in epidemiology involve different ways of writing very large numbers, especially when looking at populations; for example, a graph showing death rates for a certain illness may be per 10^5 population per year. Medical reports may involve working with very small numbers and compound measures; for example, concentrations may be in parts per million (ppm).

It may be necessary to establish the appropriate units and scales for measuring or presenting numerical information, or using estimation and working with appropriate degrees of accuracy. It will also mean that you can understand and work with powers. Studies involving epidemiology may mean working with large data sets.

What you must know
Part 1: The Learning Curve will help you with the knowledge you need.

What you must do
Part 2: The Bottom Line will help you with the evidence you need

Further opportunities for evidence: tracking care shares

If you look in the financial section of the broadsheet newspapers (e.g. *Guardian* and *Times*) you will see stock market listings. One of the sections includes details on companies in the health sector. Look at the examples in the chapter on evidence from everyday sources to see what number evidence can be generated by tracking this share index.

Hospitality and Catering Vocational A-level

About the specifications

The Hospitality and Catering awards include the study of food and drink, accommodation and front office, customer service, purchasing and cost control, and practical investigations of hospitality and catering outlets and industries.

Topic area 1
Investigations into hospitality and catering industry

Planning and interpreting information

When trying to establish the importance of the industry nationally, you will have an opportunity to gather a range of different numerical information from tables, graphs, charts and other sources. When understanding and interpreting employment trends, there will also be an opportunity to interpret numerical information.

Here are some useful sources:

- Trade magazines and periodicals will be an extremely useful source of accurate and up-to-date numerical information concerning the industry. Trade magazines will also be useful in securing numerical information involved in food and drink and information that may involve ingredients, costs, etc. There may also be numerical information on tariffs, trade restrictions and quotas that are important to the hospitality and catering sector
- Government statistics often give data on the size of the industry, how much money it makes and how many people are employed.

Calculating

In reading and manipulating statistics to do with the hospitality and catering industry, there will be opportunities to carry out multi-stage calculations. This might be particularly the case if you are going to project the results of predicted percentage growth or reduction of the industry (or an aspect of it) over time. This might allow you to establish justifiable predictions about the changes on employment or in the contribution made to the UK economy.

Interpreting results and presenting information

You should be able to justify a lot of the results from investigations into the hospitality and catering industry by using number information that you have found or by presenting the results of calculations that you have done.

You could to do this by showing the contribution the sector makes to the British economy comparing it to other key sectors. This comparison

could be done with regard to numbers employed in the industry, the financial contribution it makes to the country and in the contribution it makes to trade and tourism. There might also be an opportunity to look at the contribution made in comparison with other European Union countries.

By taking a comparative approach, there will be an opportunity to convert the statistics or data into pie charts. You will also be able to use graphs if you are predicting trends.

You must make sure the information you present has been generated by you and is not just a copy of information that has been gathered elsewhere. Using government statistics might be an opportunity to show that you are able to round figures up or down using appropriate degrees of accuracy. It will be worth looking at how different sources of statistics, like the government, round the larger numbers as well.

Topic area 2
Purchasing, costing and control

Remember that producing an accurate forecast may be useful in generating evidence for interpreting, calculating and presenting information, all geared towards a common purpose.

Planning and interpreting information

There will be an opportunity to use and interpret purchasing documentation and stock control and consumption reports; these too will provide numerical information. There will also be budgets.

Calculating

There will be an opportunity to perform calculations using costs that relate to profit and loss. This will involve understanding with and calculating material costs, labour costs (which will include salaries, wages, staff benefits and taxation), overheads, fixed and variable costs, direct and indirect costs and apportioned costs.

There are also several opportunities to generate number information when you look at calculating costs and prices or products and services. This may involve using given rates of gross profit, applying set mark-ups and applying service charges and discounts as well as calculations concerning VAT. This will show that you can work out proportional change. Remember VAT at 17.5% can be added to totals by multiplying by 1.175.

Monitoring and controlling costs and sales will also provide evidence. This will involve forecasting, use of appropriate degrees of accuracy and the need to continually monitor and interpret numerical information that may be constantly changing.

These activities all contain opportunities for working with amounts and sizes, scales and proportions and rearranging and using formulas.

Purchasing, costing and control may also provide opportunities to work with large data sets, perhaps spreadsheets or tables with over 50 items.

Interpreting results and presenting findings

You will have an opportunity to present numerical information that is a result of your calculations using industry-accepted ways. Though you will be encouraged to generate summaries of sales and costs, such as profit and loss and trading statements, and forecasts of business performance, such as budgets, occupancy levels and covers served, these summaries will be enhanced by effective use of appropriate graphs, charts and diagrams. These ways of presenting numerical information used in the hospitality and catering industry will also be effective when making comparisons or showing trends.

Further opportunities for evidence

You will find that some optional units will be much better than others for generating Application of Number evidence at level 3. There will be opportunities to take units that develop themes which relate to costing, purchasing and control. Some units might also require you to do some detailed forecasting.

Look at how your Application of Number portfolio is building up and how you intend to ensure that you are providing evidence for all types of multi-stage calculations (amounts and sizes, scales and proportions, handling statistics, rearranging and using formulas). There might be optional units that will help you generate evidence to plug any gaps in your coverage of the requirements.

If you are intending to use your Hospitality and Catering GNVQ as the only source of evidence for your Application of Number key skill, then it is important that you have a clear picture of how you will cover all the requirements. When there is a choice of units, you should try to base your selection on what you are interested in, what you might need to help you progress to higher education or employment, and what might help you provide more key skills evidence (especially evidence that might be missing from your portfolio).

Good sources of numerical information for hospitality and catering include:

- Instruments for measuring and weighing like scales and timers, measuring in everyday units like litres and grams; using measuring jugs.
- Numerical information found in recipes, e.g., quantities of ingredients and cooking times.
- Numerical information found on food packaging, e.g. typical values of energy, fibre, fat; amounts per serving and amounts per 100 grams; kilojoules (kj) and kilocalories (calories).
- Costs and prices, differences between wholesale and retail prices etc.

Units about diet or food groups provide useful opportunities to present numerical information concerning typical food values using graphical methods.

What you must know
Part 1: The Learning Curve will help you with the knowledge you need.

What you must do
Part 2: The Bottom Line will help you with the evidence you need

Opportunities

Information and Communication Technology Vocational A-level

About the A-Level syllabus

There is a clear relationship between the content of the Computing A-level and that of the Information and Communication Technology (ICT) Vocational A-level so the following text is relevant to both awards.

Your course may include the study and the application of different methods of representing numbers. In addition to the denary system (base 10) it may include binary (base 2), hexdecimal (base 16), representation of integers, floating point numbers, and binary coded decimal (BCD). There will also be opportunities to work with data communication, the INTERNET and a range of different hardware and software.

You should also look at working on course work or projects as a major opportunity to generate number evidence. This is partly because you are in charge of some of the direction your work takes, so you can lean towards numbers more heavily if you wish. This may have the added benefit of improving the quality of your computing work and the depth of your understanding about the area.

About the Vocational A-level award

The ICT Vocational A-level will often have a different emphasis on how you use the knowledge, skills and understanding that you gain in doing the course. It will also adopt a more applied approach, emphasising the vocational interpretation of the content and trying to help you understand how IT is used in the working world.

Remember to look at optional units as a chance to continue generating number evidence and keep in mind that some optional units will be better than others for creating number opportunities. If you have some influence over the optional units you can take you should keep this in mind as one factor to help you choose.

Topic area 1
Don't overlook the obvious

When you use (or especially when you buy) a computer you are constantly bombarded with different ways of talking about, using and presenting numbers. You may need to compare the capacity and speed of access of various media like magnetic tape and disk, optical media and CD-ROM. This is a basic numbers comparison and should provide you with lots of opportunity to generate evidence.

When your course looks at principles of electronic data communication and modems, there will be opportunities using a whole series of numbers relating to average connection speeds (bps), average download speed (Kbps). These are both compound measures used to express numbers (see the planning and interpreting requirements in the key skill).

Your course may start with a look at BIOS systems and the initial BIOS screen on your PC will show the basic numbers important to the machine. Here you can look for opportunities to generate number evidence and make sure you understand the basic numbers important to the machines you use.

The following information was taken from an American computing magazine and was used to describe a notebook (laptop) computer:

- 750 MHz AMD K6 CPU
- 64 MB SDRAM (192 MB max)
- 1 MB L2 cache, 8 MB VRAM
- 14.1 active matrix XTG display
- 16 GB UDMA hard drive, 1.44 MB floppy
- 12.2 × 10.1 × 1.97 inches, 7.95 pounds
  (the USA still uses imperial measurements)
- one-year warranty ($2345 rrp).

This list includes all sizes and types of numbers. When you come to look at hardware, or better still make comparisons, you will get all sorts of opportunities to interpret, calculate and present using these numbers. You work with approximation the entire time. Look at the following information on real memory quantities.

Term	Abbreviation	Approximation	Real size
Byte		1	1
Kilobyte	K or KB	1 000	1 024
Megabyte	M or MB	1 000 000	1 048 576
Gigabyte	G or GB	1 000 000 000	1 073 741 824
Terabyte	T or TB	1 000 000 000 000	1 099 511 627 776

Topic area 2
Working with number bases

Planning and interpreting information
Here are some of the opportunities:

- Explaining the use of different number bases and other number representations requires you to make decisions about what stages are involved, how you will clearly show the processes, and what presentation techniques you can use.
- The interpretation of complex tables required by the Key Skills specification occurs naturally when translating between number bases. You may also be reading other forms of graphics.
- You will also be producing evidence needed for the Key Skill as you explain and demonstrate how computers handle very large and very small numbers.

- Representation of negative integers by two's complement and sign and magnitude method and describing the conventions for storing negative values and the use of two's complement to perform subtraction.

In particular, look for opportunities when you:

- Explain the conversion of denary to binary and use hex as shorthand for binary
- Work on representation of integers and fixed point numbers
- Work with binary coded decimal and explain BCD format and its advantages
- Compare the precision and range of various number systems, according to their representation.

Calculating

The key skill requirement to show methods clearly and work to appropriate levels of accuracy coincides with your course requirement for clarity and accuracy in describing and working with number systems. The nature of the topic requires you to consider the precision of various number systems and their representation.

You will probably use practical examples to explain the representation of numbers and translation between different forms. You should consider examples which include the following types of evidence:

- Multi-step calculations
- Use of powers and roots
- Working with large data sets
- Working with formulas

There may also be opportunities to gather evidence if you work on:

- Rounding errors and truncation errors
- Floating point numbers lead to the concept of mantissa and exponent, the need for normalisation and how normalising affects the range and precision of the number represented.

Interpreting results and presenting findings

To explain the different ways in which numbers are represented and handled by computer systems, you will need to accurately interpret the system and select appropriate methods of presenting the information. Graphic forms such as comparison tables could be used to help you in your explanations.

Your course may require you to discuss and consider the merits of various number systems and their representation. If so, this will help generate evidence for the key skill which asks you to show you can make critical judgements about numbers.

Topic area 3
Working with spreadsheets

You may find that in working with spreadsheets you are able to pick up number evidence to show that you can handle statistics, deal with complex data and carry out calculations using formulas. This really depends on the nature of your work and the focus of your activity. However, you may find there is an opportunity to generate evidence for number if you check your computer work, if you double-check results by annotating your printouts, or even if you are in the development and design stages and are carrying out some preparatory work.

Spreadsheet work will provide several different opportunities to show you can present data effectively and appropriately. This will also allow you to examine critically and justify your methods and the selections you made. Your spreadsheet work could be used to show you can construct and label charts, graphs and diagrams correctly and that you are able to use them to draw appropriate conclusions. Look for opprtunities to present results in the following graphical forms:

- Line graphs
- Bar charts
- Pie charts
- Use of picture markers
- Scatter charts

Show that you can present charts and line graphs appropriately, including the use of:

- Chart or graph title
- Axis labels
- Background
- Legend data series label
- Data labels
- Category labels
- Axis formats
- Axis values
- Gridlines.

Land and Environment Vocational A-level

About the specifications
The Land and Environment awards include the study of topics like investigating the land and environment sector, the science of plant and animal management and monitoring and managing ecosystems.

Opportunities

See also: **Biology A-level**, page 56

Topic area 1
Plant and animal management

Evaluating the effects of environmental conditions and nutrition on plant growth and the success of husbandry methods may mean there are opportunities to generate evidence for the key skill on planning and interpreting information from two different types of sources. It may even involve working with a large set of data.

If you are determining how plant functions alter in response to light intensity, air temperature and wind speed, there may also be an opportunity to show you can make reliable and accurate observations, using suitable equipment and measuring in a variety of appropriate units. This may even mean working with compound measures, another level 3 requirement.

Plant nutrition and feeding may mean working with very small numbers (e.g. when looking at plant feed ingredients, and you may find there are compound measures that are particularly appropriate to this aspect of land and environment. Animal management will involve similar number opportunities but the focus will be more geared towards dietary needs.

You will find that technical and trade magazines will contain some fairly complex number information about a range of factors e.g. information on yield, feed and pricing. They may also contain statistics and comparative information that involve a range of number uses and they may present statistics in several different ways. Crop information can get quite technical and complex. You may find that these sources of information are useful to help you reach the level 3 standards.

Enterprise production means giving consideration to commercial factors, such as the costs associated with particular husbandry methods, and the type of plant or plant product that the market demands. Try to use this as a potential opportunity to generate calculations. You will probably need to extend the vocational requirements to begin to meet the key skill needs; however, this may mean strengthening your vocational work, creating opportunities for higher grades.

You must be able to identify the costs of the production methods used, financial return, and success in meeting market requirements, over a given period of time (e.g. a production cycle), including labour costs.

Topic area 2
Monitoring and managing ecosystems

The vocational unit's requirements may ask for evidence that you can collect and analyse primary data (e.g. surveys) and present the results. You will be asked to ensure that all your survey data is accurate and all your calculations are accurate. Vocational requirements may also ask you to use methods that communicate your primary research data both statistically and graphically or using other visual methods. These types of activities have a clear relationship with the requirements of the number key skill.

By reflecting on your choice of methods, in calculating and presenting your information, and by checking the accuracy of the data collected, the calculations you made and the data you present, you may also be able to generate better quality vocational evidence. This means you stand a better chance of producing quality work suitable for getting higher grades.

Carrying out an ecological survey will mean working with and applying the following techniques used to survey population diversity and distribution:

- Random sampling.
- Controlled sampling (e.g. transect).

Methods of environmental monitoring and measuring for light, temperature, humidity and pH will mean making reliable and accurate observations. Selecting and applying techniques used to survey populations and for environmental monitoring means choosing appropriate methods and justifying your choices. There will also be an opportunity to carry out multi-stage calculations to do with amounts and sizes and handling statistics.

Topic area 3
Investigating the land and environment sector

This may mean looking at the economic contributions made by the land and environment industry. Areas that would be particularly useful for generating number evidence include:

- The sector's contribution to gross national product.
- The value of exports and imports.
- The numbers employed in the sector as whole, e.g. employment trends.
- Comparisons with other major UK industries.

When evaluating the impact of land and environment businesses on the UK economy, you may have a chance to plan and interpret information from two different types of source, perhaps even including a large set of data. The particular focus for carrying out calculations is likely to be performing multi-step calculations to do with amounts and sizes, scales and proportions and handling statistics.

You may find more ideas for generating number evidence by looking at the other Vocational A-levels that have a similar unit.

Other ideas when working with plants

You may have to work with instrumentation to interpret and record light, temperature, water, levels of nitrogen, phosphate and potash and pH levels.

Packaging for fertiliser or chemicals carries information on weight, percentage values of ingredients and amounts to be used per area of land; this

provides further opportunities. On a smaller scale, most plant food has detailed information about:

- Ratios and proportions to be used when it is dissolved in water; these might change with the solution volume, the application frequency and the plant type.
- How many grams to be used per square metre, or ounces per square yard; this involves working out areas and volumes, converting measurements, etc.
- Analysis of ingredients (e.g., total nitrogen and other elements used); this might involve converting between fractions, decimals and percentages.

When looking at husbandry systems look out for opportunities to work with numbers in explaining yields, production levels and input levels of fertilisers and agrochemicals. With fertilisers and chemicals you could look at the amounts and how much land they can cover. This will mean working with areas and units of measurement, for the amounts of fertiliser and chemicals used, and for the number of acres they can be used on. This will involve conversion of measurements between systems like number of kilos per acre, and it will involve working out areas and volumes.

Plant food often involves working out the number of millilitres (ml) of food to the number of litres of water (proportions and ratios). This can be converted into imperial measures (fluid ounces, pints and gallons).

What you must know
Part 1: The Learning Curve will help you with the knowledge you need.

What you must do
Part 2: The Bottom Line will help you with the evidence you need

Leisure and Recreation Vocational A-level

About the specifications
The Leisure and Recreation awards include the study of topics like marketing and investigating the travel and tourism industry.

Topic area 1
The travel and tourism industry

Planning and interpreting information
There will probably be three main opportunities to interpret information when studying the sports industry.

- The scale and economic importance of sports
- Funding of sports
- Major trends in each sport

The scale of sport and its contribution to the UK economy
As a major employer the sports industry has people who are self-employed and those employed directly by sports organisations. Surveys can provide a useful way to show the proportion of the UK population that takes part in or watch sport.

You need to be aware of numbers of people employed in sport, numbers of people who participate in a range of sports and the contributions that sport makes in terms of annual spending in the UK population. This will help you with meeting the key skills on reading and understanding graphs, complex tables and charts; but you need to focus on the word 'complex' for level 3.

Try to use graphs and tables which show the sports information you need and which are appropriate for your level 3 number portfolio. However, the various information sources you will need to access will help you with the key skill on obtaining relevant information.

The organisation and funding of sport

The provision of sport can be at local, regional, national and international levels. You will probably be asked to show that you understand how sport is organised and funded; you need to understand the major sources of funding for most sports and the organisation and funding of sport at international, national, regional and local levels. This will also provide opportunities to generate evidence, but try to make sure the sources are at an appropriate level.

Trends in sport

You need to recognise or determine trends and understand the reasons for them. This may provide further opportunities to interpret number information. Trends are likely to involve:

- Sporting activities with increasing participation or decreasing participation.
- Changing markets for sporting activities, e.g. the 'ageing population' and improved health has resulted in more retired people staying active for longer.

Conducting an investigation into sports would constitute a substantial and complex activity, giving you an opportunity to break it down into a series of tasks.

At level 3 you will need to show that you are capable of reading and understanding more complex graphs, tables and charts. Try to do this by getting hold of government statistics, preferably data that involves comparisons with other countries or looks at changes over time. Sometimes the European Commission produces useful data that compares the member countries.

Calculating

Given the data you may have collected, you may be able to enhance your vocational evidence and generate number information by:

- Working out proportional change.
- Using large data sets and calculating averages and ranges.
- Determining rates of growth for participation rates or percentage changes to funding levels; this will help with the multi-step calculation aspects of the level 3 requirements.

Opportunities

The importance of sport for the mass media includes audience size and audience profile. This could involve working with numbers and handling different statistics.

Interpreting results and presenting findings

You might be asked to show a major trend in a sport or to explain using statistics the economic significance of sports in terms of financial turnover, number of participants or numbers employed. This will give you an opportunity to demonstrate you can use appropriate methods to illustrate findings, show trends and make comparisons.

Topic area 2
Marketing

You might be asked to do some market research. This could mean designing a research strategy, implementing it and analysing the data and reporting your findings, showing you can:

- Classify customers into key segments (e.g. by using standard industry socio-economic groupings such as age, family circumstances and lifestyle).
- Conduct primary research (e.g. surveys, observation and focus groups) and secondary source research.
- Analyse findings (e.g. from sampling, questionnaires, data analysis and survey results).

You may also be asked to identify the strengths and weaknesses of the key primary and secondary research methods.

This type of exercise could give you an opportunity to plan a substantial and complex activity by breaking it down into a series of tasks. It will also provide a wealth of opportunities to generate evidence of interpreting, calculating and presenting your number work.

You should also look at the other areas in this part that have marketing as an opportunity for evidence (e.g. Business, Retail and Distributive Services); they may have useful ideas for you. Also have a look at Travel and Tourism.

Plugging gaps in your evidence

What you must know
Part 1: The Learning Curve will help you with the knowledge you need.

What you must do
Part 2: The Bottom Line will help you with the evidence you need

When looking at the local sports picture, you might be able to establish how much is spent per person from the local authority budget on a particular sport, or you might be able to determine how much sports ground there is per square metre for each person. This could involve working with scale drawings of the locality and determining actual measurements and sizes, rounding up or down as appropriate. You could work out how much is spent on sports per person. It really depends on the quality of the data you are able to find.

How much water is there in your local swimming pool? This volume calculation may not be quite as simple as you think – the pool probably has a shallow end and a deep end. If your local pool is a weird and wonderful shape then break it down into smaller more regular shapes to make the calculation easier; it will also show that you are capable of making good approximations and you can choose appropriate and acceptable degrees of accuracy. Convert it from metric to imperial (conversion between systems).

Manufacturing Vocational A-level

About the specifications
The Manufacturing award includes the study of manufacturing at the broad national level and at the level of individual organisations and particular products they make. There are opportunities to study products and processes in terms of design, production planning, costing, health and safety, environmental impact, energy use, quality assurance and control. Optional units allow you to focus your studies on these topics.

Topic areas 1
Investigating manufacturing organisations
Investigating manufacturing processes
Approaches to quality assurance and control

See also: **Design and Technology A-level**, page 67

Planning and interpreting information
In several of the Vocational A-level units you will be investigating national manufacturing sectors, organisations within sectors and you will be assessing their processes, their quality procedures, and their effect on the environment.

The data you use will be written, numerical and graphical data of various types relating to the economy, to manufacturing, and to activities within an organisation. Some of the information will involve large data sets such as financial and economic reports, and product quality data. Other data might relate to life-cycle analysis of processes, use of energy, and approaches to quality assurance.

You will need to plan what aspect of an organisation and what process you are going to study and select appropriate data for calculation and for presentation. Remember to keep evidence to show that you had a choice of sources and data, and remember to note how you chose the most appropriate items for your investigations.

Calculating
In describing the economic contributions of organisations you are likely to be analysing company accounts and analysing statistical data associated with the local economy and the national economy. You will also need to convert information to quantities, percentages and other comparisons that are effective.

Your investigation will involve financial decisions taken about aspects

of production, with a record of the calculations used in making the decision. These calculations are likely to involve financial formulas such as those associated with costs, profits and return on capital.

To evaluate product quality you will typically need to process statistical data and calculate results such as averages and standard deviations. Other calculations will relate to analysis of a process and its use of energy. Remember to keep records of all calculations.

Interpreting results and presenting findings

The results of your investigations into various aspects of manufacturing organisations and processes will require a variety of techniques to interpret them and to present them. The key skill requirement for a graph, a chart and a diagram should be easy to meet. Opportunities include showing:

- Structure and functions of organisations and links within them.
- Contributions to the economy.
- System and flow diagrams for manufacturing processes.
- Flow diagrams for energy in processes.

Topic areas 2
Designing and developing products
Production planning and costing
Using production plans and manufacturing

Planning and interpreting information

Several units in the Vocational A-level involve investigations into the design and manufacture of particular products. You will therefore encounter a variety of information and techniques such as the following:

- Analysing market research and product information to develop a design specification.
- Planning and scheduling of production such as by using critical path analysis.
- Preparing to use plans and schedules.

You need to plan efficient techniques for your purpose and be able to interpret the information gained, such as by correctly understanding relationships and units.

Calculating

To make use of your information you need to carry out calculations, such as the following:

- Carrying out multi-step calculations to do with scales and proportions using appropriate conventions, standards and projections.
- Calculating quantities, dimensions and shapes of materials and components required for production.
- Carrying out calculations to do with quantities, costs, selling price and resources.

Interpreting results and presenting findings

You will need to present the results of your investigations and you should have a good choice of opportunities to illustrate research findings and to make comparisons between various design and production options. Here are some typical opportunities:

- Producing a final design solution accompanied by drawings.
- Choosing findings you wish to highlight and selecting appropriate graphical methods to show these findings
- Using, graphs, charts, diagrams and drawings with appropriate labels and scales.
- Presenting quantities, costs, statistics and other results to give information about a product or process.

Equally as important as the presentation of your findings are drawing appropriate conclusions based on your findings and relating them to the purpose of your investigation. You also need to be able evaluate and justify the methods that you used. Did they produce useful results? Are there better methods?

Media: Communication and Production Vocational A-level

About the specifications

The Media awards include the study of topics like media marketing and investigating the media industries. When you are studying media, it is not always obvious where your number evidence will come from. You will need to keep careful track of your progress as you build up your evidence, taking care to note any aspect of the key skill you have not yet covered.

By identifying gaps early, you will have more time to identify other opportunities to generate the number evidence. You will probably have to use a range of opportunities from compulsory and optional units, maybe other courses as well, in order to meet the whole of the number requirements. However, when opportunities do present themselves in the media course, you should make the most of them and exploit them fully.

Topic area 1
Marketing

You should look at the ideas for generating number evidence in marketing, highlighted in the other areas as well (e.g. Business, Retail and Distributive Services, Travel and Tourism).

The media marketing evidence is unlikely to ask directly for any number work; however, the ability to interpret and manipulate number data is a key part of marketing. You may find that by working number skills and evidence into your media evidence, you help improve your understanding of marketing and improve the quality of your vocational

evidence, generally. For example, showing you have a firm grasp of the financial aspects and implications of marketing may well help you meet grading requirements. For higher grades you might be asked to explain the implications of implementing a marketing strategy. Your number work may help you add more details.

Producing a marketing strategy for a media product would constitute a substantial and complex activity (a key skill requirement). It provides you with an opportunity to show you can break down the task into a logical series of smaller tasks. However, if it is to be used as number evidence, remember the focus of the activity should be using numbers and numerical data to help develop the marketing strategy.

While working on developing a marketing strategy, you may well be asked to collect information on audiences and possible competitors using primary and secondary research methods. This will provide you with an opportunity to show you can:

- Obtain relevant information from different sources.
- Make accurate and reliable observations.
- Read and understand complex tables, graphs and charts.
- Choose appropriate methods for obtaining the results you need.

Topic area 2
Media industries

Employment patterns and ownership patterns, even if this particular topic area were to be externally assessed, you would find that by focusing some of your number portfolio efforts on this topic you would:

- Cover some important ground in helping you revise the topics and gain a better understanding of the area to be assessed.
- Have an opportunity to brush up your skills in reading and interpreting graphs, tables, charts and diagrams and actually be able to create them yourself. By actually representing important information about employment patterns and trends or ownership patterns using graphs and charts you are doing the best form of revision possible – actually doing it yourself. This is especially important because the external assessment may present information in this way and then ask you questions about it.

Further opportunities for evidence

Pre-production and production
Whether it is audio, audiovisual or print, there will be elements of costing and budgeting to consider and you should capitalise on opportunities like this to help build your number portfolio. You may also find that some optional units are better than others at generating number evidence; this might be something you at least consider if you have a say in selecting optional units.

Conducting media research

This is likely to involve conducting questionnaires or surveys and using other primary research methods and secondary sources as you prepare research documents. Depending on the nature of your statistics you may end up working with a large data set, helping you meet another part of the key skill requirements. If geared towards a clear purpose, your research would also constitute a substantial and complex activity.

Having generated information, you will also have a chance to analyse results of questionnaires and prepare presentation material. This will help you meet the key skill on interpreting results of your calculations, presenting your findings and justifying your methods. You should try to use collecting and presenting your own data as a chance to create at least one graph, one chart and one diagram.

What you must know
Part 1: The Learning Curve will help you with the knowledge you need.

What you must do
Part 2: The Bottom Line will help you with the evidence you need

Performing Arts Vocational A-level

About the specifications

The Performing Arts awards do have opportunities to generate number, but there are potentially fewer than in other courses. This means that you need to keep careful track of your progress, as you generate your number evidence. When opportunities arise in your performing arts course you should take them and try and make the most of them.

If you are keen to maximise your chances of generating number evidence in your performing arts course, you should also consider selecting optional units more likely to help you generate evidence. Otherwise, keep a look out for opportunities in other courses or activities you do that may also be able to generate number evidence.

Opportunities for evidence

Conducting research into how economic factors have influenced a performance piece you have created can provide opportunities to generate number evidence. Having found out this type of information, you can then look at how best to present it.

Calculations that are particularly relevant to performing arts include:

- Amounts of revenue from productions
- Proportions of production budget for different cost headings
- Statistical data about audiences
- Profit and loss for a production run

Investigating the funding needs of a planned event or production can also provide potential opportunities.

Investigating audiences for events and performances can mean generating your own statistics through a range of primary methods or accessing

secondary research data. This may be your chance to show that you can work with large data sets and that you are able to manipulate the information appropriately to show different averages, the range of the data and other statistical information.

If you are organising events, think about:

- Gathering information about the costs involved (eg marketing, wages, hiring venue and equipment, set and costumes) and possible sources of funding.
- Surveying audience preferences in relation to your events and performances.
- Calculating a potential budget, including revenue, expenditure, break-even point and profit margin.
- Calculating audience statistics.

This would allow you to interpret results from your calculations, present your findings and justify your choice of methods. You could use this as an opportunity to use graphs, charts and diagrams. Presenting could involve:

- Budgets with information explaining your decisions
- Factors about audience preferences

Possible number benefits

You might find that although there are occasions to generate number evidence when working towards meeting your vocational pass requirements, the number work is too low-level or not essential. You need to remember that by exploiting every opportunity, you may actually be showing that you are capable of meeting some of the higher vocational grading requirements. There may be benefits in pursuing opportunities, extending them to show you can work with more difficult or complex situations or data.

Showing that you can generate more detailed number information about your performing arts studies and that you can produce more complex number data or interpret complex sources of numerical information those may:

- Improve the quality of your vocational work.
- Show that you are capable of working more independently.
- Show you have a greater depth of understanding of the performing arts topics you are studying.

These may be listed in your vocational unit grading requirements.

What you must know
Part 1: The Learning Curve will help you with the knowledge you need.

What you must do
Part 2: The Bottom Line will help you with the evidence you need

Retail and Distributive Services Vocational A-level

About the specifications
The Retail and Distributive Services awards include the study of topics like finance, marketing and investigating developments in the industry.

See also: **Business A-level**, page 59

Topic area 1
Marketing

Planning and interpreting information

The creation of a marketing plan provides an opportunity to plan a substantial and complex activity, breaking it down into a series of tasks. You might be able to conduct primary research (surveys, use of sampling, pilots and field trials) to determine the current image of organisations. In identifying, collecting and use primary and secondary data, there will be clear opportunities to get involved with planning and interpreting information from different sources. This may also include large data sets of over 50 items. This could be published data or data you generate yourself.

Working with marketing databases might be a useful way to show you can work with a large set of data (over 50 items). The key skill asks that at some point you use a large data set. Databases can also provide information about customer behaviour – customer preferences and buying patterns, sales trends for new and existing products, product substitution. All these things may involve interpreting numerical information. They may also contain numerical information about the market, e.g. market share, market segments and competitor activities. You will also have an opportunity to look at sales, turnover, profit and volume, and all involve numbers.

Calculating

Pricing and techniques like penetration, skimming, cost plus and the difference between value and price may involve multi-stage calculations. There will also be opportunities to show your methods clearly and work to appropriate levels of accuracy.

Larger data sets may involve using measures of average and range to compare distributions, and to estimate mean, median and range of grouped data. Working with primary and secondary data will provide opportunities to use checking procedures that identify errors in your methods and the results they generate.

You may need to look at the information collected and predict the possibilities for growth in sales, forecast percentage increases, and consider various possibilities and scenarios. You might be asked to suggest methods of improving an organisation's sales, turnover, profit and volume.

Interpreting results and presenting findings

The marketing strategy can be written up using graphical methods to support the points made and to enhance the overall impact and effect of the proposals. You could also use graphical methods of presenting information during any oral presentation of your marketing plan. When interpreting numerical information from other sources, look at how the source presents it then decide how you might modify the presentation for your purposes.

Topic area 2
Finance in retail and distributive services

In creating evidence to show how finance is administered and managed, there will be opportunities to generate number evidence to show that you can interpret information, make necessary calculations and work out clear ways of presenting your work.

Planning and interpreting information

Financial reports are based on a range of documents used to control financial activities. You may have an opportunity to review and interpret these types of reports and the different types of numerical information they contain. This might mean working with balance sheets and profit and loss accounts.

Budgeting, forecasting and costing information may also be available to you. This will provide you with an opportunity to show you can interpret a range of information containing numbers to meet your purpose.

Looking at the financial performance of a business, using a range of financial data (including information from ratios and shareholder returns) and then drawing conclusions from your findings, this is one exercise that would take you through all three aspects of the key skill.

See also: **Business Vocational A-level**, page 88

Sales and financial information can be used to forecast and budget. To learn how to do this, you need to know how retail and distribution organisations produce forecasts, including how to construct and use trading (sales) forecasts and budget forecasts. You need to be able to construct them yourself and you may get an opportunity to interpret this type of information from real-life examples. By constructing these types of forecast you will be generating information for the calculating part of your portfolio and you will be presenting numbers using appropriate methods.

Calculating

Constructing simple accounts, simple balance sheets and profit and loss accounts will mean having to understand and work with:

- Budgeting
- Forecasting
- Costing

Recording this financial information will provide opportunities for gathering evidence. You may be asked to record this using electronic and manual methods, presenting it using appropriate methods (a number requirement).

Again, there will be opportunities to generate calculations as you learn how to construct and use administrative controls such as:

- Sales ledger
- Purchase ledger
- Nominal ledger

You may also learn how costs are measured and classified, looking at costing and pricing. This will help you understand how organisations construct forecasts from such financial data. Look for opportunities to show you can carry out multi-stage calculations and perhaps work out proportional change. Opportunities to work with spreadsheets may mean a chance to re-arrange and use formulas, equations and expressions.

There may also be a range of different opportunities to generate calculations when you learn about measuring financial performance, and when you look at how organisations manage their business in respect of profit levels and profit centres (profit share, shareholder dividends). In learning about how business performance is measured, you will learn how to construct the following items and you should have further opportunities to generate number evidence:

- Balance sheets
- Profit and loss accounts
- Cash flow analysis.

Interpreting results and presenting findings

You may have to depict trends or make comparisons, show performance (e.g. share price) or even work out how best to present complex financial information for business reports. These opportunities will show that you can chose appropriate methods; construct appropriate charts, graphs, diagrams and tables; and use labels and accepted conventions appropriately and effectively.

Topic area 3
Developments in retail and distributive services

Look for opportunities to work with economic trend data and information and statistics about consumer behaviour. There may also be opportunities to work with data showing changes in employment patterns.

Comparison and trend work tends to create good opportunities to present information using a range of different methods, and you may wish to use these topics for addressing this aspect of the key skill.

Investigating shopping patterns nationally and in your local area could also create similar opportunities to gather information, analyse your results and present your findings.

What you must know
Part 1: The Learning Curve will help you with the knowledge you need.

What you must do
Part 2: The Bottom Line will help you with the evidence you need

Science Vocational A-level

About the specifications

The units of the Vocational A-level Science award includes investigation of the types of science, organisations and people involved in the workplace and investigation of their links with the community and the economy. The award also includes units that increase your knowledge of particular scientific areas by carrying out practical investigations and linking the results to relevant industrial processes. Other units allow you to make extended

scientific investigations into chosen areas of science or aspects of the scientific workplace.

See also: **Biology A-level**, page 58

Topic areas
Investigating the science workplace
Monitoring the activity of the human body
Controlling chemical processes
Controlling the transfer of energy
Synthesising organic and biochemical compounds

Planning and interpreting information

In carrying out all investigations you will need to start by planning your approach, breaking it into manageable tasks and interpreting data. The following types of activity will produce the evidence needed for the key skill:

- Using paper-based and computer-based information systems.
- Identifying, measuring and recording indicators of physiological status.
- Selecting and interpreting data about energy use in systems.
- Selecting and interpreting data related to chemical processes.
- Interpreting representations of three-dimensional molecular shapes.

Some of the information will involve large data sets such as results of readings and surveys. Remember to keep evidence to show that you were able to select and interpret information to help your investigations.

Calculating

To make use of your results from observations, measurements and other data you will need to carry out calculations. Here are some possible areas of activity connected to the key skill:

See also: **Chemistry A-level**, page 61

- Processing statistical results from data such as sets of physiological indicators.
- Establishing health norms for individuals.
- Calculations associated with chemical processes such as rates of reaction, equilibrium constants, enthalpy changes.
- Calculating the yields and results of volumetric analyses.
- Using formulas associated with energy transfer, such as for calculating improvements in efficiency.
- Calculating fluid flow rates.
- Working with ratios and scales when interpreting results and presenting your findings.

These activities will help you meet the requirements of the key skill, e.g. knowing how to use formulas. You also need to know about possible sources of error in your methods and your results such as the natural errors in instruments and in your methods of using them.

Interpreting results and presenting findings

You will need to present the results of your investigations and you should have a good choice of opportunities to illustrate your findings, to show trends and to make comparisons. Here are some typical activities:

- Preparing and presenting findings about local organisations to show their type of work and structures.
- Presenting risk assessments for activities you carry out risk assessments relating to industrial or environmental applications of science.
- Presenting statistical data, trends and other results using charts and graphs.
- Interpreting the results of calculations associated with chemical processes such as rates of reaction, equilibrium constants and enthalpy changes.
- Presenting the features of a system and its transfer of energy.
- Describing compounds showing structures and nomenclature.
- Explaining appropriate background knowledge, such as chemical and biochemical principles.
- Choosing findings you wish to highlight and selecting appropriate graphical methods to do this.

These activities will normally involve the range of interpretation and graphical techniques required by the key skill. Equally as important as the presentation of your findings are drawing appropriate conclusions based on your findings and relating them to the purpose of your investigation. You also need to be able evaluate and justify the methods that you used. Did they produce useful results? Are there better methods?

See also: **Physics A-level**, page 81

Opportunities from optional units

Most scientific investigations provide good opportunities to collect evidence for the key skill. The organisation of the key skill into preparation, calculation and presentation is the same basic format used for an experiment or other scientific investigation.

Investigations of organisations or processes may need analysis of costs or financial aspects. These activities provide good evidence for the key skill, such as by tracking and analysing the stock market performance of companies engaged in technology. Look at the examples in the chapter on evidence from everyday sources.

What you must know
Part 1: The Learning Curve will help you with the knowledge you need.

What you must do
Part 2: The Bottom Line will help you with the evidence you need

Travel and Tourism Vocational A-level

About the specifications
The Travel and Tourism awards include the study of topics like the marketing and investigating the travel and tourism industry.

Opportunities

Topic area 1
Investigating the travel and tourism industry

Planning and interpreting information

The national Government and local government, as well as market research agencies, produce a number of different sources of information that show information like:

- Estimated attendance of different tourist attractions.
- The contribution the leisure and tourism sector makes to the local economy and the national economy.
- The number of people employed in the industries.
- Increases in visitors, numbers employed or money made over a period of time.

All of these statistics will also involve different ways of rounding numbers and approximating.

Newspapers carry financial information on the performance of leisure and hotel stocks and shares. You could invest an imaginary amount of money in your sector, choosing your companies and seeing how well they perform over a certain length of time (e.g. month). This will allow you to interpret the information about the shares as they appear in the newspaper, then invest your money and calculate how well it is doing, showing it on a graph.

Alternatively, you could track performance of just one company over the course of a month, checking the share price once or twice a week.

See also: **Geography A-level**, page 72

Calculating

When you look at the scale of the UK travel and tourism industry, you will be working with and handling key industry statistics connected with:

- UK travel and tourism revenue
- Employment statistics
- Incoming tourist numbers to the UK
- Travel statistics for UK residents

An analysis of travel and tourism stocks and shares will give you some appreciation of the importance of the travel and tourism sector to the private sector. Working with shares will give you a number of opportunities to calculate at level 3. You can work out the percentage increase or decrease of the share prices, or how much money could have been made or lost had you bought some shares and sold them a month later.

The Financial sections in newspapers show a range of share information about the levels of trading and volume of share trading. There will be a several level 3 opportunities to interpret, calculate and present a range of numbers connected with private sector travel and tourism. If this is a particular interest, you can pursue it further in more specialist newspapers like the *Financial Times* or periodicals like the *Economist*.

Interpreting results and presenting findings

All the suggestions above will create opportunities to present your work using different graphical methods. You will also have an opportunity to select methods that are the most effective and appropriate. As you describe the scale of the UK travel and tourism industry and its economic significance, you will need to quote relevant data. It will help to present appropriate information using diagrams, charts or graphs. This will allow you to support your vocational evidence and generate key skills work.

Topic area 2
Marketing

You might be asked to do some market research. This could mean designing a research strategy, implementing it and analysing the data and reporting your findings, showing you can:

- Classify customers into key segments (e.g. by using standard industry socio-economic groupings such as age, family circumstances and lifestyle).
- Conduct primary research (e.g. surveys, observation and focus groups) and secondary source research.
- Analyse findings (e.g. from sampling, questionnaires, data analysis and survey results).

You may also be asked to identify the strengths and weaknesses of the key primary and secondary research methods.

This type of exercise could give you an opportunity to plan a substantial and complex activity by breaking it down into a series of tasks. It will also provide a wealth of opportunities to generate evidence of interpreting, calculating and presenting your number work.

You should also look at the other areas in this part that have marketing as an opportunity for evidence (e.g., Business, Retail and Distributive Services); they may have useful ideas for you. Also have a look at Leisure and Recreation.

What you must know
Part 1: The Learning Curve will help you with the knowledge you need.

What you must do
Part 2: The Bottom Line will help you with the evidence you need

Opportunities

Evidence from everyday sources

When you are confident with numbers you will not even realise that you are using them. Numbers become so much a part of finding out, making clear and doing the job, they just seem to occur naturally. This chapter is dedicated to showing you how numbers and your use of them are already a part of your everyday life. It will also help you to generate number evidence from situations not related to qualifications.

Using information

This chapter uses everyday information to show how you:

- Use information and data already.
- Can use information and data more effectively.
- Could find out more from the information and data you have.
- Can present information and data to help others understand what you mean.

Practising your number skills

Each example has real text containing information or data which is simplified to show you how it is really number in action. Numbered lists identify what you should know, understand or do and they link these three skills with the information shown in the real text.

Personal tasks and topics

This shows how you can take the experience you have gained from the topic and prepare and plan your own investigations to produce authentic and valid evidence for your Application of Number portfolio.

The topics

The ten topics are intended to provide examples of where you can find numbers if you begin to look for them. They are not the only places you will use numbers on a daily basis. Find examples of your own and see how much you take for granted the skills you have and how much you can develop these skills and understand more about the power and influence numbers have on your everyday life.

Opportunities

Weather matters

The weather report opposite is taken from a regional newspaper. You can find weather reports like this in national newspapers, on teletext and on the internet. This type of information is a rich source of numerical, graphical and written information and together with information taken from the sources listed above, it can be used to create the large data set (over 50 items) expected at level 3.

Using information

The information can be used for a range of purposes but it will be most useful if the activity is meaningful to you. This could include travel arrangements or other studies, including geography.

Please check that you can read and understand how numerical information is provided by the different charts and tables. Note especially how the same information appears in both charts and tables because the city is part of more than one category.

Practising and using your number skills

Look at the key below to see if you can read, understand and use the information to develop your number skills.

1. This chart shows the temperature range for England, Scotland, Ireland and Wales. Can you say what the group size is?
2. This chart shows Western Europe using the same temperature groupings. What information does it give you at a glance?
3. This table gives you the °C/°F temperatures of prime holiday destinations today. It provides a simple focus for those seeking quick access to information. All temperatures are given as 'high'
4. This table is similar to the one containing holiday destinations although its focus is worldwide.
5. This table gives a two-day forecast for the top travel destinations
6. Some cities are mentioned more that once as they have readings for today, tomorrow and the day after. Present them in a table and give the mean temperature and range for the three days.
7. Use the range categories under the map to construct a frequency table for temperatures worldwide over these three days. Use the means you found in point 6 for cities mentioned more than once. Use the frequency table to construct a frequency diagram and show the median temperature for the destinations. Can we say that this is a good representation of the worldwide average temperature for these three days? Explain your answer.

Personal tasks and topics

The opportunities provided by the example are intended to help you

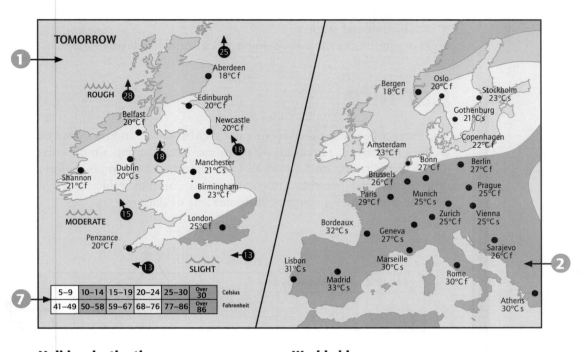

TOMORROW

(1)

Aberdeen 18°C f
25
ROUGH 28
Edinburgh 20°C f
Belfast 20°C f
Newcastle 20°C f
18
18
Shannon 21°C f
Dublin 20°C s
Manchester 21°C s
Birmingham 23°C f
MODERATE
15
Penzance 20°C f
London 25°C f
13
13
SLIGHT
13

Bergen 18°C f
Oslo 20°C f
Stockholm 23°C s
Gothenburg 21°C s
Copenhagen 22°C f
Amsterdam 23°C f
Bonn 27°C f
Berlin 27°C f
Brussels 26°C f
Paris 29°C f
Munich 25°C s
Prague 25°C f
Zurich 25°C f
Vienna 25°C s
Bordeaux 32°C s
Geneva 27°C s
Sarajevo 26°C f
Lisbon 31°C s
Marseille 30°C s
Rome 30°C f
Madrid 33°C s
Athens 30°C s

(2)

5–9	10–14	15–19	20–24	25–30	Over 30	Celsius	
41–49	50–58	59–67	68–76	77–86	Over 86	Fahrenheit	

(7)

Holiday destinations

	°C	°F			°C	°F	
Barbados	26	79	showers	Malaga	28	82	fair
Bermuda	30	86	fair	Miami	24	75	thunder
Benidorm	28	82	fair	Naples	27	81	fair
Bordeaux	27	81	sunny	Palma	29	84	cloudy
Corfu	27	81	cloudy	Rhodes	27	81	sunny
Florence	28	82	sunny	Rio de Jan	34	93	sunny
Gibraltar	24	75	sunny	S.Francisco	18	64	sunny
Ibiza	29	84	fair	Seychelles	27	81	cloudy
Jo'burg	23	73	sunny	Sicily	28	82	fair
Luxor	35	95	sunny	Tenerife	28	82	fair
Marseille	28	82	sunny	Trinidad	32	90	showers

(3)

Worldwide

	°C	°F			°C	°F	
London	22	72	cloudy	Lisbon	29	84	sunny
Amsterdam	23	73	cloudy	Madrid	27	81	sunny
Athens	30	86	fair	Melbourne	15	59	cloudy
Barcelona	28	82	sunny	Moscow	23	73	fair
Budapest	20	68	showers	Munich	24	75	fair
Buenos Aires	17	63	fair	New York	26	79	cloudy
Cairo	29	84	fair	Nice	26	79	sunny
Cape Town	14	57	rain	Oslo	19	66	fair
Crete	27	81	sunny	Paris	25	77	sunny
Faro	27	81	sunny	Rome	27	81	sunny
Hong Kong	31	88	fair	Stockholm	23	73	fair
Istanbul	24	75	fair	Sydney	16	61	fair
Jerusalem	28	82	fair	Tokyo	33	91	cloudy
L' Angeles	20	68	fair	Midday reading today			

(4)

Top travel destinations – two day forecast

Amsterdam
Tomorrow (C/F)
Fair,
High 23 73
Low 15 59
Saturday
Fair,
High 22 77
Low 15 59

Athens
Tomorrow (C/F)
Sunny,
High 30 86
Low 21 70
Saturday
Fair,
High 29 84
Low 21 70

Brussels
Tomorrow (C/F)
Fair,
High 26 79
Low 14 57
Saturday
Sunny,
High 27 81
Low 15 59

Copenhagen
Tomorrow (C/F)
Fair,
High 22 72
Low 12 54
Saturday
Fair,
High 21 70
Low 13 55

Frankfurt
Tomorrow (C/F)
Fair,
High 28 82
Low 15 59
Saturday
Sunny,
High 28 82
Low 14 57

Helsinki
Tomorrow (C/F)
Sunny,
High 22 72
Low 9 48
Saturday
Sunny,
High 19 66
Low 7 45

Madrid
Tomorrow (C/F)
Sunny,
High 33 91
Low 15 59
Saturday
Sunny,
High 32 90
Low 15 59

(6)

Moscow
Tomorrow (C/F)
Sunny,
High 22 72
Low 11 52
Saturday
Fair,
High 19 66
Low 9 48

New York
Tomorrow (C/F)
Thunder,
High 26 79
Low 18 64
Saturday
Cloudy,
High 23 73
Low 18 64

Paris
Tomorrow (C/F)
Fair,
High 29 84
Low 15 59
Saturday
Fair,
High 30 86
Low 15 59

Rome
Tomorrow (C/F)
Fair
High 30 86
Low 17 63
Saturday
Showers,
High 29 84
Low 17 63

Stockholm
Tomorrow (C/F)
Sunny,
High 23 73
Low 9 48
Saturday
Sunny,
High 21 70
Low 9 48

Vienna
Tomorrow (C/F)
Sunny,
High 25 77
Low 14 57
Saturday
Fair,
High 25 77
Low 14 57

Zurich
Tomorrow (C/F)
Fair,
High 25 77
Low 11 52
Saturday :
Sunny,
High 25 77
Low 11 52

(5)

understand how to work with tables and charts of this type, especially how to group data, present these findings graphically and explain the outcomes – not just mathematically but also in terms of sense and reality.

Charts, tables and diagrams like these are available in all newspapers and magazines. They can be collected over a period of time and used to obtain data for a specific purpose, including:

- Geography coursework
- Environmental studies
- Planning journeys or choosing a place to live or visit.

Car hire

The extract below is taken from a holiday brochure and its shows car hire charges for certain European destinations. You can find similar advertisements in the press, on teletext and through motoring organisations. This type of material presents information in a complex table. It is complex because it provides a range of different sets of data on:

CAR HIRE (1 Sept 2000 to 31 Aug 2000)			Low season				High Season			
RESORT	MODEL	MAX OCC.	PRICE PER CAR IN £'S		PRICE PER EXTRA DAY		PRICE PER CAR IN £'S		PRICE PER EXTRA DAY	
			3 DAYS	7 DAYS	3 +	7 +	3 DAYS	7 DAYS	3 +	7
ANDALUCIA	Fiat Punto	4	70	102	19	19	70	102	19	19
	Seat Ibiza	5	80	133	20	20	80	133	20	20
	Opel Astra	5	90	143	24	24	90	143	24	24
CANARY ISLANDS	Renault Clio 3 door	4	69	118	19	18	69	118	19	18
	Seat Ibiza 1.4 5 door	5	72	123	20	19	72	123	20	19
	Seat Cordoba 5 door	5	94	173	27	26	94	173	27	26
THE ALGARVE	Renault Twingo 3-door	4	69	109	19	18	76	147	20	19
	Ford Fiesta 5-door	5	73	116	20	19	79	157	21	20
	Fiesta Automatic 5-door	5	100	171	29	26	106	199	30	27
MADEIRA	Fiat Punto 3-door	4	96	183	30	30	96	183	30	30
	Fiat Punto, 3-door	5	100	193	31	31	100	193	31	31
	Ford Fiesta 3-door	5	112	220	36	36	112	220	36	36
MALTA	Mini 3-door	3	56	93	14	14	56	93	14	14
	Ford Fiesta 3-door	4	59	100	15	15	59	100	15	15
	Ford Fiesta 5-door	5	62	106	16	16	62	106	16	16
CYPRUS	Suzuki Alto 800	4	76	135	21	21	82	156	23	23
	Daihatsu Charade	5	80	145	22	22	87	160	25	25
	Mazda 323	5	84	155	24	24	97	186	28	28

Prices include
- Local taxes
- Unlimited mileage
- Comprehensive insurance including bail bond where applicable
- Collision damage waiver
- Personal accident insurance (only if you have taken our holiday insurance)
- Delivery (if required) 0900 to 2100

Low season
1 October to 31 October
1 April to 30 April

Charges
All charges are in pounds (£)

- Destinations
- Seasons and dates
- Models of car and numbers of passengers
- Costs, both fixed and extended

Using information

If you are able to read, understand and use this information and explain how your results and findings have been drawn from the table, you should have generated evidence for Application of Number.

Please check that you can read and interpret this table. Note how the scale of charges increase from low season to high season and how different destinations have very different rates, even for cars with the same maximum occupancy.

Practising and using your number skills

Look at the key below to see if you can read, understand and use the information to develop your number skills.

1. This is a complex table that provides you with a range of data for you to interpret, combine to produce results and check for accuracy.
2. The table is split into low season and high season. The dates for high season are found in a note at the bottom.
3. The costs of hire vary according to:
   - Maximum occupancy
   - Blocks of days
   - Supplementary days
   - Low and high season
4. The table enables you to work out charges for any number of days but is based on several assumptions to do with:
   - Normal length of hire
   - Normal size of group
5. The assumptions in point 4, can you suggest what they are?
6. The travel company's assumptions result in several inconsistencies in the scales of charges. It is often less expensive to hire a car for a set period and return it before the time is up. Can you find examples of this?

When booking a car, few individuals would think of taking a table like this and analysing the contents in depth to check out the best deal, but competitor companies would. Another company, however, which is looking to compete in this market, would. Use the information to construct a range of graphical material to set out the information for one destination. Use the tables, charts or graphs to compare the different ways of combining the information to show inconsistencies and how to get value for money.

Personal tasks and topics

Interpreting complex tables like this is an important skill. It is especially important when you are planning an activity or an event such as a holiday or a function that requires you to hire specialist facilities or equipment.

If you have an opportunity to plan and prepare an event that requires you to combine, cost and sequence a range of interrelated activities, this should provide valid evidence for the key skill at this level. Make sure you:

- Develop and update an action plan, including date for completion.
- Retain copies of your original sources such as brochures or correspondence.

- Record information clearly and accurately.
- Choose your methods and calculations carefully and organise them so that they can be read.
- Check that your results make sense in terms of the original plan.
- Ensure that your findings are clearly presented in terms of costs, dates and sequence, and that they can be understood by others.

Journeys and routes

The stylised diagram below shows the rail links between the ferry ports of Dover, Ramsgate and London and a section taken from the Sunday timetable for down trains. This type of diagram is often used to show customers where stations are in relation to each other. This table is typical of those used by transport services to provide customers with accurate and detailed information.

Portway Trains

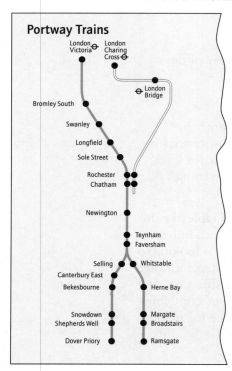

Timetable

London Victoria ⊖	dep	0841	0905	....	and at	....	1741	1805	....
Bromley South	dep	0900	0921	....	same	....	1800	1821	....
Swanley	dep	0911	....	....	minutes	....	1811	....	....
Longfield	dep	0920	....	....	past	....	1820	....	....
Sole Street	dep	0927	....	....	each	....	1827	....	....
London Charing Cross ⊖	dep	0823c	....	....	hour	....	1723c	....	....
London Bridge ⊖	dep	0830c	....	....	until	....	1730c	....	....
Rochester	dep	0936	0944	....		....	1836	1844	....
Chatham	dep	0939	0947	....		....	1839	1847	....
Newington	dep	0952	....			....	1852	....	
Teynham	dep	1001	....			....	1901	....	
Faversham	art	1007	1011	←		....	1907	1911	←
Faversham	dep	1014	1012	1014		....	1914	1912	1914
Selling	dep	→	....	1019		....	→	1919	
Canterbury East	dep	....	....	1029		....	....	1929	
Bekesbourne	dep	....	....	1033		....	....	1933	
Snowdown	dep	....	....	1043		....	....	1943	
Shepherds Well	dep	....	....	1047		....	....	1947	
Dover Priory ⛴	arr	....	....	1056		....	....	1956	
Whitstable	dep	....	1020	....		....	1920	....	
Herne Bay	dep	....	1027			....	1927	....	
Margate	dep	....	1043	....		1910	1943	....	
Broadstairs	dep	....	1048	....		1915	1948	....	
Ramsgate ⛴	arr	....	1054			1920	1954	....	

c   Change at Chatham.
⛴   Shipping service.
⊖   Stations having interchange with London Underground services.
→   Continued in later column.
←   Continued from earlier column.

Using information

The timetable can be described as a complex table because it holds a variety of different information using numbers and symbols that need to be decoded and interpreted for use. The rail network of stations is a simple way of representing information. The diagram is not an accurate representation of distance or route; it represents only the position of each station in relation to another.

Please check that you can read and understand both the table and the diagram and that you can see how they relate to each other.

Practising and using your number skills

Look at the key below to see if you can read, understand and use the information to develop your number skills.

1. This type of route map is called a schematic drawing or diagram. It shows the relationship or sequence of all the stations on the route. A rail link like this is often called a network. What would be the nodes and arcs?
2. This is typical of a section taken from a timetable. Can you work out where the train divides and how this is represented on the table?
3. This is a key to help you find out additional information about your train journey and the facilities available.
4. The diagram is not drawn to scale. Can you explain why? What is the main line London station shown here? How can you tell this? Can you combine the information on the timetable with the information in the diagram, to more accurately show the relationship between the journey and the time it takes?
5. The timetable has no specific details for trains leaving London Victoria between 0905 hours and 1741 hours. Provide a schedule for a tourist departing from London Charing Cross who wishes to arrive at Dover Priory at 1456 hours

Personal tasks and topics

This type of graphical material provides you with opportunities to:

- Extract relevant information from different sources such as schematic drawings or timetables.
- Practice interpreting complex tables using keys and symbols.
- Understand and use compound measures and scales and proportions to present information.

Data presented in this way does not require multi-stage calculations but, when combined with other sources for more substantial or complex activities, opportunities may arise such as:

- Planning a journey between two locations and comparing cost and time, as well as ease and comfort for different modes of travel, including private car or public transport. This will require detailed itineraries as well as estimations of mileage and associated costs. Findings could be presented using graphs, charts and diagrams including travel graphs.
- Travel arrangements for individuals attending an event, meeting or conference. This would include accommodation, and travel from a range of different destinations by a variety of modes of transport.

Cheques and balances

The bank statement below is for a personal account. Statements like this are usually sent to you directly from the bank every month. They provide you with a record of every transaction covered by your account.

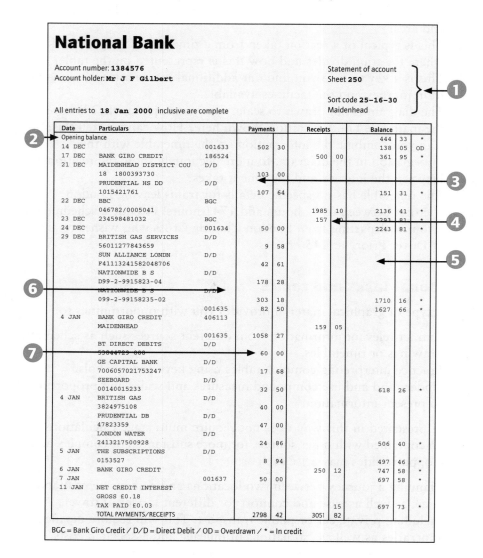

National Bank

Account number: **1384576**
Account holder: **Mr J F Gilbert**

Statement of account
Sheet **250**

Sort code **25–16–30**
Maidenhead

All entries to **18 Jan 2000** inclusive are complete

Date	Particulars		Payments		Receipts		Balance		
Opening balance							444	33	*
14 DEC		001633	502	30			138	05	OD
17 DEC	BANK GIRO CREDIT	186524			500	00	361	95	*
21 DEC	MAIDENHEAD DISTRICT COU	D/D							
	18 1800393730		103	00					
	PRUDENTIAL HS DD	D/D							
	1015421761		107	64			151	31	*
22 DEC	BBC	BGC							
	046782/0005041				1985	10	2136	41	*
23 DEC	234598481032	BGC			157		2293	81	*
24 DEC		001634	50	00			2243	81	*
29 DEC	BRITISH GAS SERVICES	D/D							
	56011277843659		9	58					
	SUN ALLIANCE LONDN	D/D							
	F41113241582048706		42	61					
	NATIONWIDE B S	D/D							
	D99-2-9915823-04		178	28					
	NATIONWIDE B S	D/D							
	099-2-99158235-02		303	18			1710	16	*
		001635	82	50			1627	66	*
4 JAN	BANK GIRO CREDIT	406113							
	MAIDENHEAD				159	05			
		001635	1058	27					
	BT DIRECT DEBITS	D/D							
	53044725 000		60	00					
	GE CAPITAL BANK	D/D							
	7006057021753247		17	68					
	SEEBOARD	D/D							
	00140015233		32	50			618	26	*
4 JAN	BRITISH GAS	D/D							
	3824975108		40	00					
	PRUDENTIAL DB	D/D							
	47823359		47	00					
	LONDON WATER	D/D							
	2413217500928		24	86			506	40	*
5 JAN	THE SUBSCRIPTIONS	D/D							
	0153527		8	94			497	46	*
6 JAN	BANK GIRO CREDIT				250	12	747	58	*
7 JAN		001637	50	00			697	58	*
11 JAN	NET CREDIT INTEREST								
	GROSS £0.18								
	TAX PAID £0.03					15	697	73	*
	TOTAL PAYMENTS/RECEIPTS		2798	42	3051	82			

BGC = Bank Giro Credit / D/D = Direct Debit / OD = Overdrawn / * = In credit

Using information

The information contained in a statement is generated by a computer. It is not infallible, so you should check the figures. This involves keeping records of your:

- Planned expenditure using direct debit.
- Expenditure via a cheque book, based on your cheque book stubs.
- Expenditure using your debit card, based on credit card receipts.

- Expected income via bank giro credit.
- Income from other sources using your paying-in book.

In this way you can monitor your balance and plan your finances.

A bank statement is a rich source of numerical information and can provide the starting point for the substantial and complex activity required at this level.

Please check that you can read and understand how number is used as code, as reference and as measure in this document.

Practising and using your number skills

Look at the key below to see if you can read, understand and use the information to develop your number skills.

1. This is the general information about you, your bank and your account.
2. This column gives details of who or what triggered the transactions – cheques or direct debits.
3. This column gives details of, and a total for, the month's expenditure.
4. This column gives details of, and a total for, the month's income.
5. This column gives details of a running total for the month and the current financial standing of the account.
6. Look at this account and sort out the expenditure into:
   - Planned and predictable expenditure
   - Expenditure via the cheque book
7. This is this individual's only bank account. Can you suggest what this person uses to pay for goods and services, and give a reason for this?

Look at the receipts column. Can you suggest who this individual works for and their net annual income, based on this statement? Find out the difference between net and gross incomes.

Personal tasks and topics

A statement like this provides access to important personal data. The amount and range of data increase when you bring together the statements for a whole year and combine them with other savings books or investment statements.

Working on your personal finances can provide you with discrete evidence for planning and interpreting information, carrying out calculations or interpreting results and presenting findings. However, you may have the opportunity to combine these tasks in a substantial activity when you review your personal finances before deciding to:

- Buy something substantial such as a car or mortgage.
- Take out a loan and meet a repayment schedule.
- Go to university and pay for tuition and accommodation.
- Take out personal insurances or set up new direct debits.

These are real activities based on your own finances. However, there is

nothing to stop you simulating an activity like this by using someone else's financial data.

To meet the evidence requirements of the key skill, make sure that you present your findings clearly and effectively and that you understand and can explain your findings to others either orally or in writing.

Additives and calories

Three pieces of graphical material taken from a variety of sources are shown below. This material provides information on:

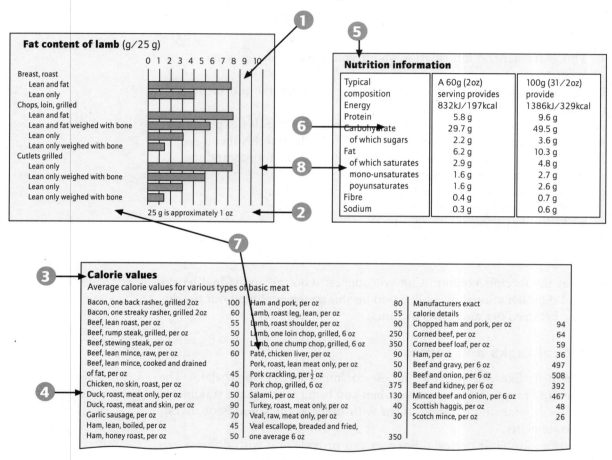

Fat content of lamb (g/25 g)

0 1 2 3 4 5 6 7 8 9 10

Breast, roast
    Lean and fat
    Lean only
Chops, loin, grilled
    Lean and fat
    Lean and fat weighed with bone
    Lean only
    Lean only weighed with bone
Cutlets grilled
    Lean only
    Lean only weighed with bone
    Lean only
    Lean only weighed with bone

25 g is approximately 1 oz

Nutrition information

Typical composition	A 60g (2oz) serving provides	100g (3 1/2 oz) provide
Energy	832kJ/197kcal	1386kJ/329kcal
Protein	5.8 g	9.6 g
Carbohydrate	29.7 g	49.5 g
of which sugars	2.2 g	3.6 g
Fat	6.2 g	10.3 g
of which saturates	2.9 g	4.8 g
mono-unsaturates	1.6 g	2.7 g
poyunsaturates	1.6 g	2.6 g
Fibre	0.4 g	0.7 g
Sodium	0.3 g	0.6 g

Calorie values

Average calorie values for various types of basic meat

Bacon, one back rasher, grilled 2oz	100	Ham and pork, per oz	80	Manufacturers exact calorie details	
Bacon, one streaky rasher, grilled 2oz	60	Lamb, roast leg, lean, per oz	55		
Beef, lean roast, per oz	55	Lamb, roast shoulder, per oz	90	Chopped ham and pork, per oz	94
Beef, rump steak, grilled, per oz	50	Lamb, one loin chop, grilled, 6 oz	250	Corned beef, per oz	64
Beef, stewing steak, per oz	50	Lamb, one chump chop, grilled, 6 oz	350	Corned beef loaf, per oz	59
Beef, lean mince, raw, per oz	60	Paté, chicken liver, per oz	90	Ham, per oz	36
Beef, lean mince, cooked and drained of fat, per oz	45	Pork, roast, lean meat only, per oz	50	Beef and gravy, per 6 oz	497
		Pork crackling, per 1/2 oz	80	Beef and onion, per 6 oz	508
Chicken, no skin, roast, per oz	40	Pork chop, grilled, 6 oz	375	Beef and kidney, per 6 oz	392
Duck, roast, meat only, per oz	50	Salami, per oz	130	Minced beef and onion, per 6 oz	467
Duck, roast, meat and skin, per oz	90	Turkey, roast, meat only, per oz	40	Scottish haggis, per oz	48
Garlic sausage, per oz	70	Veal, raw, meat only, per oz	30	Scotch mince, per oz	26
Ham, lean, boiled, per oz	45	Veal escallope, breaded and fried, one average 6 oz	350		
Ham, honey roast, per oz	50				

- The fat content of different cuts of lamb
- The calorie counts of meat and poultry
- The nutritional information from a food packet

Using information

Information like this is available in books, magazines and on foodstuffs. It is now a legal requirement for food to carry this type of information. It can be used for a range of different purposes:

- To check out additives in foods in case of allergies.
- To ensure a balanced diet for people with special requirements such as the very young or the elderly.
- To meet an individual's special dietary requirements, e.g., an athlete.

The information provided here will be sufficient for the purposes identified above or as part of an Application of Number programme but the ability to interpret charts and tables like these will enable you to research and obtain relevant information from a variety of different but associated sources.

Please check that you can read and understand the tables and graphs. Do you understand the relationship between grams and ounces and ounces and calories?

Practising and using your number skills

Look at the key below to see how you can use the information presented in a range of different formats, using different compound measures to develop your understanding of how numbers are used.

1. This graph or bar chart shows the fat content of different cuts and preparations of lamb. It uses an approximate scale where 25 grams are equivalent to 1 ounce. Can you find the real relationship?
2. This graph is an approximation only because it simplifies the relationship between grams and ounces to make the figures easy to read. Assume that the relationship between fat and the 25 gram scale is accurate. Use the data you have here to find the percentage error between the equivalence of grams and ounces and use it to increase the fat readings proportionately. Now use this data to construct a more accurate histogram
3. This table shows the calorie count for different cuts and preparations of a range of meat and poultry. It provides you with the opportunity to give a compound measure of calories per ounce for those meats that do not give readings per ounce.
4. Look at the table of meats and poultry and their calories. Choose an appropriate method to group this data, e.g., according to meat type, and find the mean and range of each group. Present this grouped data in a way that compares the mean calorie counts for each meat type. Use the data you have collected, the grouped data, the mean and ranges you have found, together with your graphs, to explain your findings.
5. This chart is taken from a meat wrapper. Note the relationship it gives between ounces and grams. Is it the same as the graph of fat content? Is it more or less accurate?
6. The Nutrition Information contained in the chart can be used to show how an average portion is made up. Represent this information graphically.
7. Select information from the graph and the table on lamb to match equivalent cuts and preparations. Show the information on calories

and fat content graphically so the relationship between cut, calorie and fat content is clearly presented.

8. Convert the information given in grams into ounces. Give your answers correct to two decimal places. The graph in point 1 uses 1 ounce equals 25 grams and the chart in point 5 uses 1 ounce equals 30 grams. Use this information to discuss the sources of error in these sets of information.

Personal tasks and topics

This type of graphical material provides you with access to large sets of data. Any investigation of foodstuffs will provide an extensive range of data that may be collected, interpreted, manipulated, presented and explained. This type of information is of particular relevance in the study of:

- Health and Social Care Vocational A-level
- Food Technology A-level
- Sport and Recreation Vocational A-levels
- Hospitality and Catering NVQ and Vocational A-level
- Other science covering foodstuffs

Flights and destinations

The tables below are taken from a holiday brochure. They are typical of those used by airlines and tour operators to provide travel agents and holidaymakers with a range of information.

Using information

Many variations of flight and traveller details are contained in these tables; this often makes them difficult to read and understand, especially if you are unfamiliar with information presented in this way.

A table like this is described as complex because it contains numbers and words used in a range of different ways and for a range of different purposes. The tables provide information on:

- Departures and destinations
- Flight advice and airline codes
- Calendar and timetable for flights
- Fixed flight supplements (£)

Tables like these will provide you with opportunities to develop your reading, interpreting and presentation skills. They are unlikely to provide enough information for a substantial task on their own. To do this, you will need to use them in combination with other sources of information (such as those discussed elsewhere in the 'everyday sources' section).

The numbered circles ①②③④⑤⑥ point to parts of the tables below.

EAST MIDLANDS

Flight	Departure	Return		Airline	LOW	MED	HIGH
TO THE ALGARVE (FAO) Flying time 2hrs 45mins							
2TP10	Thu 15.40	Thu 14.40	6 May-28 Oct	AMM	22	29	45
TO ANDALUCIA (AGP) Flying time 2hrs 40mins							
2TF10	Fri 15.00	Fri 14.00	7 May-29 Oct	AMM	35	39	57
TO CORFU (CFU) Flying time 3hrs 20mins							
2TG00	Mon 07.00	Mon 14.30	3 May-25 Oct	AMM	29	39	65
TO CYPRUS, Larnaca (LCA) Flying time 4hrs 35mins							
2TK20	Sun 16.00	Mon 02.35	2 May-31 Oct	AMM	39	49	82
TO CYPRUS, Paphos (PFO) Flying time 4hrs 35mins							
2TK40	Wed l9.15	Thu 05.30	24 Mar-27 Oct	AMM	29	35	63
TO FUERTEVENTURA (FUE) Flying time 4hrs							
2TC90	Wed 08.40	We 17.50	24 Mar-27 Oct	AMM	NIL	NIL	NIL
TO GRAN CANARIA (LPA) Flying time 4hrs 15mins							
2T32	Sun 23.55	Sun 23.20	2 May-31 Oct	AEA	23	28	47
TO LANZAROTE (ACE) Flying time 4hrs 10mins							
2TC72	Thu 14.40	Thu 13.40	25 Mar-17 Jun	IWD	19	24	42
2TC72	Thu 14.40	Thu 13.40	22 Jul-28 Oct	IWD	19	24	42
TO MALLORCA (PMI) Flying time 2hrs 25mins							
2TA10	Mon 09.40	Mon 08.50	17 May-25 Oct	AEA	35	41	57
2TA20	Tue 16.40	Tue 15.40	4 May-26 Oct	IWD	32	37	55
2TA60	Sat 09.15	Sat 14.55	1 May-30 Oct	AMM	59	65	92
2TA62	Sat 19.20	Sat 18.30	1 May-30 Oct	AEA	46	51	75
2TA68	Sat 23.55	Sat 23.15	1 May-30 Oct	AFA	33	39	67
TO MALTA (MLA) Flying time 3 hrs 15 mins							
2TM02	Tue 17.35	Wed 01.00	4 May-26 Oct	AMM	22	29	49
TO MENORCA (MAH) Flying time 2 hrs 30 mins							
2T870	Fri 08.25	Fri 14.05	7 May-29 Oct	AMM	35	39	62
TO RHODES (RHO) Flying time 4 hrs 25mins							
2TH12	Wed 20.25	Wed 07.00	5 May-27 Oct	AMM	25	35	59
TO SORRENTO (NAP) Flying time 2 hrs 35 mins							
2TC40	Fri 15.05	Fri 21.40	7 May-29 Oct	AMM	15	19	37
TO TENERIFE (TFS) Flying time 4hrs 35mins							
2TC20	Fri 23.35	Fri 22.35	26 Mar-29 Oct	FUA	29	35	59
2TC22	Fri 13 05	Fri 12 05	26 Mar-29 Oct	IWD	35	39	63
TO TURKEY, Bodrum (BJV) Flying time 3hrs 55mins							
2TT14	Mon 10.20	Mon 09.30	3 May-25 Oct	POT	39	45	67
TO TURKEY, Dalaman (DLM) Flying time 4hrs 5mins							
2TT34	Mon 22.40	Tue 08.25	3 May-25 Oct	AMM	25	32	59

GATWICK

Flight	Departure	Return		Airline	LOW	MED	HIGH
TO THE ALGARVE (FAO) Flying time 2hrs 45mins							
OTO	Thu 07.00	Thu 13.00	6 May-28 Oct	MON	9	12	35
OTP18	Sat 13.05	Sat 19.15	27 Mar-30 Oct	FCL	19	25	55
OTP22	Sun 16.25	Sun 22.30	28 Mar-31 Oct	MON	12	17	39
OTP24	Sun 07.00	Sun 13.30	2 May-31 Oct	MON	19	25	49
TO ANDALUCIA (AGP) Flying time 2 hrs 25 mins							
OTF10	Fri 06.00	Fri 11.50	2 Apr-29 Oct	FCL	NIL	NIL	NIL
OTF20	Sat 13.15	Sat 19.15	27 Mar-30 Oct	FCL	20	25	54
OTF22	Sat 09.30	Sat 16 00	1 May-30 Oct	MON	20	25	54
OTF24	Sat 07.10	Sat 13.10	1 May-30 Oct	FCL	22	27	54
OTF26	Sun 09.00	Sun 15.25	2 May-31 Oct	MON	24	29	56
TO CORFU (CFU) Flying time 3hrs 10mins							
OTG00	Mon 06.30	Mon 13.45	3 May-25 Oct	MON	19	24	47
OTG04	Mon 22.15	Sun 05.15	3 May-25 Oct	MON	9	15	35
OTG10	Fri 06.55	Fri 13.50	7 May-29 Oct	FCL	23	28	58
OTG14	Fri 22.30	Sat 05.30	7 May-24 Sep	FCL	18	24	53
TO COSTA BRAVA (GRO) Flying time 2hrs							
OTD40	Sun 06.20	Sun 11.00	2 May-31 Oct	FCL	6	12	25
OTD50	Fri 16.50	Fri 21.30	7 May-24 Sep	FCL	NIL	NIL	NIL
OTD50	Fri 14.30	Fri 21.20	28 May-8 Oct	CKT	2	5	15
TO CRETE, Chania (CHQ) Flying time 4hrs							
OTH76	Tue 10.15	Tue 19.00	4 May-12 Oct	FCL	NIL	NIL	NIL
TO CRETE, Heraklion (HER) Flying time 4hrs							
OTH70	Tue 17.40	Wed 02.05	4 May-26 Oct	FCL	9	14	35
OTH72	Tue 14.10	Tue 23.10	4 May-26 Oct	AMM	15	19	39
OTH74	Tue 22.50	Wed 07.25	4 May-26 Oct	FCL	NIL	NIL	NIL
TO CYPRUS, Paphos (PFO) Flying time 4hrs 15mins							
OTK42	Wed 18.15	Thu 04.15	5 May-27 Oct	DP	NIL	NIL	NIL
OTK40	Wed 07.00	Wed 16.15	5 May-27 Oct	FCL	22	29	62
OTK52	Tue 07.00	Tue 16.50	4 May-26 Oct	FCL	15	22	55
OTKL6	Wed 13.00	Wed 00.30	5 May-27 Oct	CKT	7	12	25
TO CYPRUS, Larnaca (LCA) Flying time 4hrs 15mins							
OTK10	Wed 09.00	Wed 19.20	24 May-27 Oct	DP	22	29	62
OTK16	Wed 07.00	Wed 17.00	5 May-27 Oct	FCL	17	23	SS
OTK18	Wed 17.00	Thu 03.20	5 May-27 Oct	DP	NIL	NIL	NIL
OTK22	Sun 15.15	Sun 01.15	2 May-31 Oct	FCL	17	19	35
TO FUERTEVENTURA (FUE) Flying time 3hrs 55mins							
OTC90	Wed 06.25	Wed 15.30	24 Mar-27 Oct	MON	9	14	29
OTC94	Wed 16.35	Thu 01.10	24 Mar-27 Oct	FCL	NIL	5	22

(Column headers for both tables: Flight supplements in £s per person for departures during — LOW, MED, HIGH)

Can you see how the numbers are used in different ways? They are used for:

- Reference in flight codes
- For times using the 24-hour clock
- For dates
- As measurements in flying times
- As amounts in supplementary costs

Practising and using your number skills

Look at the key below to see how numerical information is presented in different ways and how it all interrelates to provide detailed information.

1. These are the two different airports providing similar services for a range of destinations.
2. Each airport's flight schedules are presented as complex tables.
3. Information for each flight is read horizontally across, starting with the flight code and ending with the flight supplement during the high season.

LONGMAN KEY SKILLS · LEVEL 3 · APPLICATION OF NUMBER

Opportunities

4. Some destinations are served by both airports. Can you identify the destinations served by the three airports and present the range of options for each in a separate table, such as all the options for the Algarve?
5. These are the flight supplements for the different seasons. You are not given the base line costs anywhere in this table. Can you suggest why? Where might you find this information?
6. Each flight and destination has a very clear schedule starting with departure time. There is some information that is not necessarily in the correct order. You normally check in one hour before a flight departs. Use the data here to write a full itinerary starting with the check-in time and ending with the return landing time for someone going on a 7-night holiday.

Personal tasks and topics

This type of complex numerical information presented in graphical material provides you with the opportunity to:

- Extract relevant information from different sources such as brochures or timetables.
- Practice reading and understanding complex tables.
- Carry out multi-stage calculations to do with time.
- Rearrange and use expressions such as for finding real costs of flights, e.g. flight during the low period is represented by $C = x + y$, where c = cost, x = base cost, y = low period supplement.
- Construct and label charts using accepted conventions such as rearranging and presenting flight information to serve an agreed purpose.

All of these are essentially discrete tasks but may be used as part of a more substantial activity that combines various tasks such as:

- A project on travel and tourism for Vocational A-levels or BTEC Nationals.
- Part of an NVQ in Customer Services or Tourism.
- Part of your job in a travel agency.
- Using these skills to interpret information from complex tables relating to other aspects of your education, training or employment..

The tour

The series of maps of different sizes shown below gradually focus on a particular region. In this case it is the Orkney Islands. They are intended to show the location and relationship between the islands, the Highlands of Scotland and the rest of the British Isles. This type of material is graphical and is an important and rich source of numerical information.

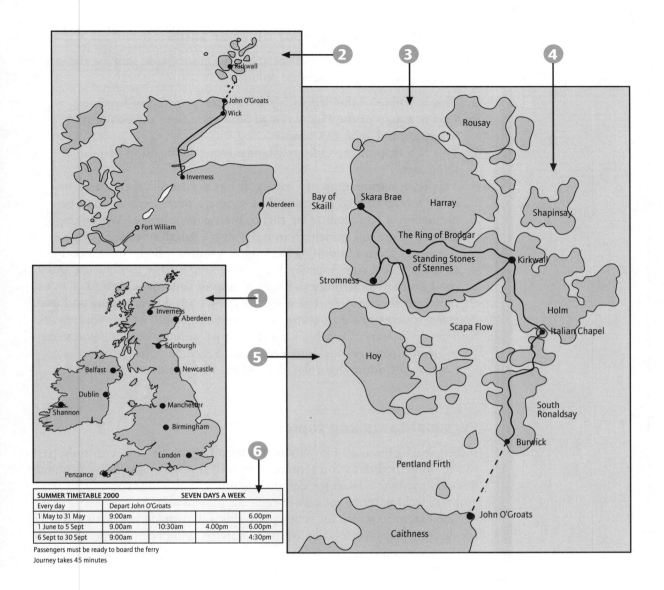

SUMMER TIMETABLE 2000		SEVEN DAYS A WEEK		
Every day	Depart John O'Groats			
1 May to 31 May	9:00am			6.00pm
1 June to 5 Sept	9:00am	10:30am	4.00pm	6.00pm
6 Sept to 30 Sept	9:00am			4:30pm

Passengers must be ready to board the ferry

Journey takes 45 minutes

Using information

You need to be able to read and understand the relationship between these different maps or diagrams and appreciate how scales and ratios can add to your understanding of the information they contain.

These maps are in a fixed ratio but no scale is given. You can use maps like these to:

- Identify locations
- Plan routes
- Estimate distances
- Use as a basis for research from other sources

Please check that you can read and understand the maps. Can you identify the Orkney Islands on the map of the British Isles?

Practising and using your number skills

Look at the key below to see if you can read, understand and use the information to develop your number skills.

1. This is a map of the British Isles. Note the position of Inverness.
2. This is a map of the Highlands of Scotland. Note the position of Inverness and John O'Groats.
3. This is a map of the Orkney Islands. Note the position of John O'Groats.
4. This is an outline map of Orkney. It has no details of contours or other topographical features. Why would a more detailed map be important if you were using this to plan your journey? Would the impact be greater on length in miles or on length of time?
5. A journey from London to Stromness requires a flight from London to Inverness, a road journey John O'Groats, a ferry to Burwick and a road journey to Stromness. Draw a map of suitable scale and represent this journey. Use a key to show each different port and use other sources of information to estimate the length of this journey.
6. This is the ferry timetable for the summer sailings. Assume you need to be in Stromness for dinner at 7 pm. Schedule your journey from London including flight details, and present this as an itinerary for travel.

Personal tasks and topics

Information presented like this will normally provide you with only part of the numerical data you require. You will need to read and understand this and use it as a basis for detailed planning that will involve identifying and researching other sources of relevant information.

The extent to which an activity like this will provide you with evidence for discrete tasks, or for a substantial activity, will depend upon the focus of the activity itself. The following suggestions could generate valid evidence:

- Planning a touring holiday involving different forms of transport.
- Planning a race for motorcycles, cars or people, involving different types of terrain, countryside or conditions.
- Researching the movements of an army during a war or planning an exercise for a cadet force.

Continuing education and training

The tables below show the fee structure, payment plan and notes on fees taken from a college brochure. This information is typical of the graphical and written material used by further and adult education organisations to promote their courses.

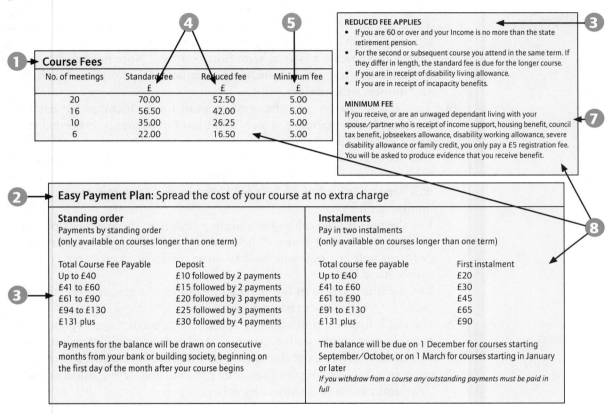

(4) **(5)**

REDUCED FEE APPLIES **(3)**
- If you are 60 or over and your income is no more than the state retirement pension.
- For the second or subsequent course you attend in the same term. If they differ in length, the standard fee is due for the longer course.
- If you are in receipt of disability living allowance.
- If you are in receipt of incapacity benefits.

MINIMUM FEE **(7)**
If you receive, or are an unwaged dependant living with your spouse/partner who is receipt of income support, housing benefit, council tax benefit, jobseekers allowance, disability working allowance, severe disability allowance or family credit, you only pay a £5 registration fee. You will be asked to produce evidence that you receive benefit.

(1) Course Fees

No. of meetings	Standard fee £	Reduced fee £	Minimum fee £
20	70.00	52.50	5.00
16	56.50	42.00	5.00
10	35.00	26.25	5.00
6	22.00	16.50	5.00

(8)

(2) Easy Payment Plan: Spread the cost of your course at no extra charge

Standing order
Payments by standing order
(only available on courses longer than one term)

Total Course Fee Payable	Deposit
Up to £40	£10 followed by 2 payments
£41 to £60	£15 followed by 2 payments
£61 to £90	£20 followed by 3 payments
£94 to £130	£25 followed by 3 payments
£131 plus	£30 followed by 4 payments

(3)

Payments for the balance will be drawn on consecutive months from your bank or building society, beginning on the first day of the month after your course begins

Instalments
Pay in two instalments
(only available on courses longer than one term)

Total course fee payable	First instalment
Up to £40	£20
£41 to £60	£30
£61 to £90	£45
£91 to £130	£65
£131 plus	£90

The balance will be due on 1 December for courses starting September/October, or on 1 March for courses starting in January or later
If you withdraw from a course any outstanding payments must be paid in full

Using information

The tables for course fees and the easy payment plan are very simple and straightforward. The written information on minimum and reduced fees is presented in plain English. The intention is that you can easily interpret the material, calculate what your fee will be and present your findings by paying the correct fee in a way that most suits you.

Individual tasks are straightforward, the complexity comes when you have to combine all three pieces of information to make an accurate payment. The example provided here will not provide you with evidence of a substantial task required by the key skill but it may meet that requirement if used in combination with information such as:

- A range of different courses
- A personal timetable or schedule

- Personal disposable income and
- A specific activity such as planning and costing a personal study programme for a year

Practising and using your number skills

Look at the key below to see how numerical information has been presented in graphical and written form.

1. This is the table of fees. Note how the information is set out in columns and rows for easy interpretation.
2. These are the tables for different payments. Note how they are set out alongside each other so you can compare them.
3. This is the written material with notes on fees. Note how this contains very important numerical information but does not include any numbers themselves.
4. The college charges you the same amount for each course for each meeting. Is this statement true? What level of accuracy is needed to make the statement true?
5. Use the information on course fees to draw constant ratio graphs on the same axes for cost against number of weeks for 6–40 weeks. You will need to use a line of best fit. How do you represent the 'minimum fee'?
6. Use the two simple tables for standing orders in the payment plan to write an expression that will help others work out how much each payment will be. You will need to write different expressions, one for each course band.
7. Use the information in the reduced fee notes to explain how anyone could be entitled to a reduced fee.
8. Use the information in all three sources to construct a complex chart or table that combines fee, payment and reduction information. You will need to select carefully which information is relevant to your chart or table. Make sure that your presentation of the information is clear and can be understood by others.

Personal tasks and topics

This type of numerical information presented in graphical and written material provides you with the opportunity to:

- Extract relevant information from different sources such as brochures and prospectuses.
- Practice reading tables and charts.
- Choose methods for obtaining results.
- Carry out multi-step calculations.
- Work out proportional change such as reductions for longer courses or more courses.
- Draw conclusions and explain results.

These skills are appropriate to other more substantial and complex tasks such as:

- Arranging and scheduling a hire purchase agreement or loan.
- Preparing and planning a complex series of events such as a sports competition or a promotional event.
- Researching and analysing scientific data from a range of sources.

Paying household bills

The next page shows a section taken from a gas bill. This is the type of household bill you will receive for all services, including electricity, telephone and perhaps water.

Using information

The type of information you receive from the utilities companies is different from advertising material. It is factual information and a bill like this must:

- Provide clear and accurate information
- Explain what the charges are based on
- State what your final charge is

A bill of this kind will not provide you with sufficient information for Application of Number at this level. When used in combination and in comparison with other bills, such as those identified above, this information can provide valid key skills evidence. Opportunities are created here for:

- Obtaining information from different sources.
- Estimation when projecting annual expenditure on services.
- Reading gas and other meters to check on consumption or to provide information.
- Understanding compound measures such as kWh and associated costs pence per kWh.
- Calculations to check and project future costs.
- Conclusions for future plans based on your understanding of information and calculations.

Practising and using your number skills

Look at the key below to see if you can read, understand and use the information to develop your number skills.

1. The bill uses numbers for reference to identify who the customer is.
2. This is the last reading taken for calculation.
3. This is the reading taken for calculating the last bill with the old price. Note that it was estimated by the gas company.
4. This is the reading taken for calculating the cost at the new price. Note that it was estimated by the gas company.

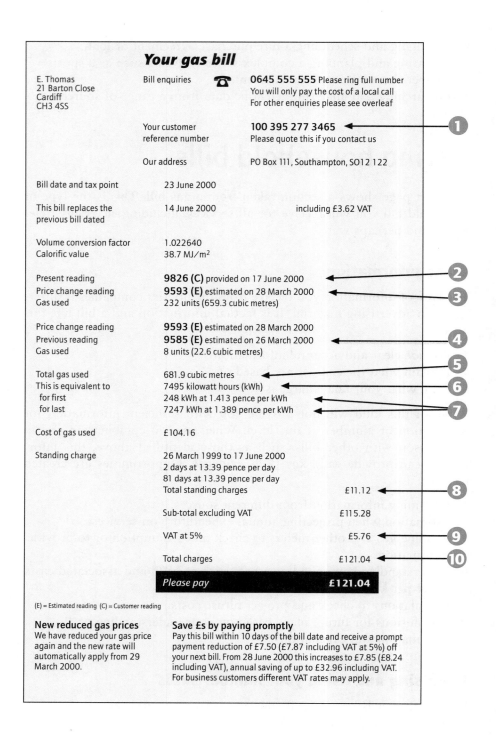

Your gas bill

E. Thomas
21 Barton Close
Cardiff
CH3 4SS

Bill enquiries ☎ **0645 555 555** Please ring full number
You will only pay the cost of a local call
For other enquiries please see overleaf

Your customer
reference number

100 395 277 3465 ◄──── **①**
Please quote this if you contact us

Our address

PO Box 111, Southampton, SO12 122

Bill date and tax point	23 June 2000	
This bill replaces the previous bill dated	14 June 2000	including £3.62 VAT
Volume conversion factor	1.022640	
Calorific value	38.7 MJ/m²	

Present reading **9826 (C)** provided on 17 June 2000 ◄──── **②**
Price change reading **9593 (E)** estimated on 28 March 2000 ◄──── **③**
Gas used 232 units (659.3 cubic metres)

Price change reading **9593 (E)** estimated on 28 March 2000
Previous reading **9585 (E)** estimated on 26 March 2000 ◄──── **④**
Gas used 8 units (22.6 cubic metres)

Total gas used 681.9 cubic metres ◄──── **⑤**
This is equivalent to 7495 kilowatt hours (kWh) ◄──── **⑥**
 for first 248 kWh at 1.413 pence per kWh
 for last 7247 kWh at 1.389 pence per kWh ◄──── **⑦**

Cost of gas used £104.16

Standing charge 26 March 1999 to 17 June 2000
2 days at 13.39 pence per day
81 days at 13.39 pence per day
Total standing charges £11.12 ◄──── **⑧**

Sub-total excluding VAT £115.28

VAT at 5% £5.76 ◄──── **⑨**

Total charges £121.04 ◄──── **⑩**

Please pay	**£121.04**

(E) = Estimated reading (C) = Customer reading

New reduced gas prices
We have reduced your gas price again and the new rate will automatically apply from 29 March 2000.

Save £s by paying promptly
Pay this bill within 10 days of the bill date and receive a prompt payment reduction of £7.50 (£7.87 including VAT at 5%) off your next bill. From 28 June 2000 this increases to £7.85 (£8.24 including VAT), annual saving of up to £32.96 including VAT. For business customers different VAT rates may apply.

5. This is the total gas used. Can you say how it is made up and how many units it comprises? Can you write down the ratio of units to cubic metres?

6. The bill is calculated using kilowatt-hours (kWh). Can you write down an expression for the relationship between cubic metres and kilowatt-hours?

7. This shows you how the cost of gas used is calculated. Can you suggest why it is calculated in this way?
8. This is your standing charge for the period of the bill. Why is it calculated for two days then a further 81 days?
9. VAT is added here. To what level of accuracy is this calculation?
10. This is the final charge. Is it correct?

Personal tasks and topics

This type of bill, which includes numbers of different sizes and a range of different units and measures, can provide you with the opportunity to:

- Practice calculating compound measures such as pence per kWh.
- Rearrange and use formulas, equations and expressions such as the relationship between units, cubic metres and costs.
- Work out proportional charge such as VAT at 5% by multiplying by 1.05.

These are essentially discrete tasks to do with different types of calculations. More substantial tasks to do with calculating household expenses will require you to collect a range of bills from a range of utilities and plan a more extended exercise such as:

- Changing from one utility supplier to another by comparing relative costs.
- Planning to change a utility from one tariff system to another to benefit from reductions such as the Economy 7 tariff.
- Breaking down household expenses so that others can contribute to payment, i.e. when sharing a flat or other accommodation.
- Presenting living costs when seeking financial assistance, such as income support.

Financial information

The next page includes a typical example of financial information taken from a newspaper on a particular day. Each day there is similar information in any newspaper, on teletext or on the internet. You may need information about a particular company or group of companies as part of an investigation into a sector of the economy.

Using information

Working with information from the financial markets provides many opportunities for collecting evidence by interpreting graphical information, analysing data, making calculations and then presenting your findings.

Opportunities

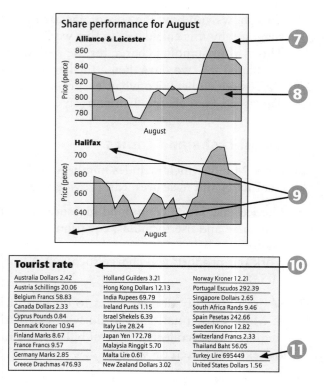

① Popular shares

	Price (pence)	Change (%)	Yield (%)
Alliance & Leicester	834	−14	3.7
Abbey National	1015	0.2	4.2
Anglian Water	734.5	1.6	7.3
British Airways	397.75	−4.1	5.5
BAA	636	0.9	3.0
BG	384	2.2	2.9
BP Amoco	1172	1.5	2.3
British Energy	500	−39	40
British Steel	169.25	−0.4	7.2
BT	951	0.4	2.7
Centrica	162	−43	N/A
Foreign & Colonial	220	2.2	1.6
Glaxo Wellcome	1681	1.9	1.6
Halifax	700	3.4	3.5
Lloyds TSB	823	−0.1	3.3
Marks & Spencer	385	3.8	4.6
Manchester United	225.75	−14	09
Norwich Union	469.25	9.8	3.4
National Power	441	−1.7	8.1
Northern Rock	445	2.3	3.4
Powergen	658	4.9	4.6
Railtrack	1199	0.1	2.8
Rolls Royce	244.25	1.0	3.4
Sainsbury	431	−0.4	4.4
Scottish Power	577	−0.3	4.9
Thames Water	860	−1.3	6.2
Thomson Travel	128.25	−5.4	3.0
United Utilities	721	−0.9	7.9
Woolwich	342.5	−1.2	3.9
Average change		−0.1	

Note: Changes are over a 7-day period

②③④⑤⑥⑦⑧⑨⑩⑪

Share performance for August

Tourist rate

Australia Dollars 2.42	Holland Guilders 3.21	Norway Kroner 12.21
Austria Schillings 20.06	Hong Kong Dollars 12.13	Portugal Escudos 292.39
Belgium Francs 58.83	India Rupees 69.79	Singapore Dollars 2.65
Canada Dollars 2.33	Ireland Punts 1.15	South Africa Rands 9.46
Cyprus Pounds 0.84	Israel Shekels 6.39	Spain Pesetas 242.66
Denmark Kroner 10.94	Italy Lire 28.24	Sweden Kronor 12.82
Finland Marks 8.67	Japan Yen 172.78	Switzerland Francs 2.33
France Francs 9.57	Malaysia Ringgit 5.70	Thailand Baht 56.05
Germany Marks 2.85	Malta Lire 0.61	Turkey Lire 695449
Greece Drachmas 476.93	New Zealand Dollars 3.02	United States Dollars 1.56

Practising and using your number skills

Look at the key below to see if you can read, understand and use the information to develop your number skills.

1. Most companies have a share price and this table is a sample taken from listings showing hundreds of companies.
2. The price of any company share continually changes so this figure is a snapshot at the end of one day.
3. This particular percentage change is taken over a 7-day period. We might also want to know the changes and the trend over a month, or over a year.
4. Some of the changes are negative, meaning that the shares have gone down in price compared with 7 days ago.
5. This is the simple average or mean. Check whether the mean is correct, to 1 decimal place. Notice how the negative numbers help balance the positive numbers so that the mean is near zero.
6. The yield figure is the income you can expect from one share. It is expressed here as a percentage of the current share price shown in the first column. Which one would you give most money on this particular day?
7. These are straightforward line graphs plotting the share price each day to show the trend over one month.
8. The graphs are filled or shaded underneath to give them more visual impact.

9. Take note of the lowest and highest figures on the vertical scale. Do you think the variations shown by the graphs are significant?
10. This 'rate' is a conversion factor used to change one currency into another; it changes each day.
11. This tells us that today the bank will give us 1.56 US dollars for one British pound.

Personal tasks and topics

Some Vocational A-level units ask you to investigate a particular sector of the economy or a particular company. The share prices in newspapers are usually grouped in sectors and the performance of the shares in a sector over a period can be used when discussing the sector or a company.

You might also invest an imaginary amount of money in your sector and see what sort of profit (or loss) you might have made over a period. You can track and plot the progress of your shares at regular intervals. This sort of task is ideal for a computer spreadsheet that can also produce instant graphs of your progress.

This type of task can provide evidence in all the key skills areas because you will be taking information from tables and graphs of shares and handling sets of data. You can then make calculations to show means, percentage changes and other comparisons, and present your results in a suitable format such as new charts and graphs.

Index